LILY

LILY

The Diary of a French Girl in New York

BY SANDRINE FORGE

GROVE PRESS, INC. NEW YORK

To Doctor Sammy Mizrahi

1

January 3rd

I lie on my stomach, my eyelids swollen and tingling, my cheek wet with saliva that shapes a round tear spot on the pillow case. I see a ray of light under the bathroom door and a transparent outline around the window. I close my eyes to the dawn. As I turn over, my arm rubs against the upholstered headboard, and I sit up, wide awake.

The bedroom is pearl gray, with a deep blue carpet. Tall dark-shaded lamps cast ominous shadows on the walls. The bay windows curve in an oval shape, suggesting faintly the prow of a ship, but I am not at sea for long; the key number on my night table reads: 2814, New Hilton Hotel, New York.

Jim Brent pushes his head under the sheet and I pull away from his kicking legs. I am wearing this stranger's shirt, the one he had on yesterday. It fits smoothly and clings to my body except for the scratchy collar. A pleasant feeling of warmth subsides on my buttocks and I see, lying on the rug on Jim's side, the pile of leather equipment responsible for that glow on my skin. On the night table, I count two vials of sleeping pills, one jar of lubricant, one bottle of baby oil, two Canadian tabloids catering to the sado-masochistic literate crowd, a few strings of rawhide my wrists and ankles still remember sorely, loose change, car keys, dinner-club cards, one pen, one comb, and a bottle of rubbing alcohol that conveyed its spruce smell from my fingers to the sheets as I was dutifully tending, last night, this man's lazy urges.

I had been referred to Lorrie Hatch, a young madam of headstrong, declining reputation, by Gene Davis, the number two heel from last year's gang. Number one was kidnaped, last Chanukah, by a Peruvian widow, who turned out to be a transvestite with a badge.

The call was made in a throaty, condescending, beauty-parlor voice, with the implication of a special job for good pay. I recalled trading with Gene a few confidences about my devotion to the whip against his own tales of similar experiences, and I had no doubts concerning the requirements I would be expected to fill. My misgivings at getting mixed up with a business girl other than Sheil opened fire against my too long estrangement from the rod, but I let the spell of the latter win and turn my insides to a throbbing pulp of fear and docility.

Conscious of the "little girl" appeal to the connoisseur in discipline, domestic or sophisticated, I chose that white blouse I now see draped over a chair, sleeves hanging down despondently. My stockings lie on the bathroom doorstep, where Jim pulled them off my legs, keeping me very still with the threat of the crop. He did fold his clothes neatly, for he undressed after tying me down on the bed, and so felt free to surrender to the delicious delays of preparations: oiling of my skin and exposure of the gluteal regions. Then on to the picking of the right props, in which he was guided by the changing tautness on my face as he dropped one strap for another.

All the while he talked to me unhurriedly about "the tribulations we masters have to go through in the training of mischievous little slave girls." He used the words of a magician who knows how to titillate the expectation and make fantasies come alive, straight from the marrow of dreams.

I found myself well out of touch with the economy of financial ethics. This one might just as well be on the house. After sitting with Jim for a mere half-hour, in Lorrie's living room, I knew this smallish, neat, slightly arrogant Philadelphian would be a man in my life and not just another price tag in my little book. His eyes, greenish-blue and watchful, flickered at me with curiosity and a challenging compassion that I resented at first. Although not clearly aware of Lorrie's gang's intentions, I could feel the air crackling with courted violence, and my gin started turning as sour as leftover butterscotch.

I was sitting on a stool, close to Jim, perched on the arm of a Récamier chair, a gold velvet mammal attired with lynx pelts. I did not know stools were his favorite racks, on which he liked to restrain his women, naked or partially disrobed, their legs spread apart, their buttocks softly divided, their right arms left free, so that he could penalize their futile attempts to protect themselves, one pleading hand waving the whip away or rubbing the sting freshly inflicted.

Lorrie praised me with the greedy gentleness of a procurer for the latest purchased victim. I learned later from Jim that, though she switches back and forth from one end of the whip to the other, she more willingly admits being

9

aggressive, in a poor try to hide her real craving: getting it. Gene Davis had changed his dirty loafers for Moroccan slippers, so displaying in debonair fashion his situation as Lorrie's protégé. (She takes him to lunch, letting her Johns pick up the tab, and is going to finance a trip he plans to Greece: "How to promote the American approach to ruffianism.") Sheree, a former business partner of Lorrie's, who recently chose the better alternative of becoming one of the very regally kept Lesbians in town, was sharing a marijuana pipe with Bernie the spider, a languid British youth, full of Zen and pimples.

They were all licking their chops, with some trouble concealing acute restlessness, and, at the same time, conveying the impression that they "only dropped in" out of boredom and would be gone with the gin they were sipping under Lorrie's crafty eyes, which bid them to be patient. Though scattered around the big room, giggling to each other from one potted plant to another, they formed a potential circle, ready to tighten and close on me as soon as Jim got up.

When Lorrie had opened the door to me, wearing a mauve terrycloth towel, a silver-bleached beehive of hair, jet-black mascara, and a cutting smile (all teeth, no glow), her apartment was empty except for us both, the smell of pot, and, among an interesting set of antiques, a tilted grandfather clock and a huge hand-painted wooden horse that distracted me all evening by being just too gorgeous to belong there.

She had tried hard to impress me and had succeeded to some degree by the snappy way she screamed on the phone to a number of girls, leafing through a fat typewritten book of numbers and names, referring to prices

10

as BQ, BK, EQ, KQ, and double O, shrieking, interrupting, and rolling over the bed in a frenzy of sarcasm, her beige cocker spaniel half-strangled in her exasperation.

As soon as she had left the phone, mellow mood succeeded fury and she was all dimples again. Pulling from a closet a handful of whips, all tangled together, she discarded the most vicious ones and told me about the job at hand:

"This John is quite a catch. He feels like working on a new girl once in a while and I'm doing him one more favor tonight by bringing you in. I expect twenty-five per cent out of your fee, which should be at least one hundred for one session. The bastard can pay for his fun. I've already milked a couple of thousand out of the slob by telling him hard-luck stories. You should get more than a hundred if you are smart. I'll make sure you don't get hurt. You have nothing to fear as long as I'm around. I want the whole stupid thing to be over early because I must go to that terrific racing-club party at the Delmonico at ten. That son-of-a-bitch should have called already. Who does he think he is to keep me waiting?"

But when the phone rang, she jumped at it in a most undignified fashion, the dog carefully stepping out of her way.

"What did you say is missing? Are you accusing me? Well, just because you are sloppy with your belongings, it's not a reason for. . . . Of course Lily is here. How long do you think we're going to wait for your fumbling afterbirth of a grand entrance?"

My hair had been set into a short pageboy with bangs, and what with navy blue and white and all, I looked properly unprofessional. I was wondering about Lorrie's age—and settling for thirty-nine—when Jim Brent came through the door. Lorrie's friends were on Jim's heels, and the conversation lingered some time around the Mediterranean patterns of culture, because of Gene's pending departure for those climes.

I was making eyes at the clock, the dog curled in my lap, feeling like a bored child made to stay in the parlor because there are guests. It was exactly the way Jim chose to put it, smilingly, in my ear. From that point on, I did not feel I was on duty any more. I even lost the whipping from mind and when, on a pretense of looking around the apartment, Jim Brent took me to the bedroom, it dawned on me that I was here for specific monetary purposes. I was invited to state my price. I named the figure Lorrie had told me to request. Jim then asked whether I was ready for the limitations we would be made to trespass if we were to stay here and entertain Lorrie's pals. Because he had some experience with such people, he knew he might not be able to control their need for excess, as well as his own, which was likely to be kindled by contagion. We could skip that risk, he added, by getting out quickly and gracefully. Get out we did, and though we were speedy enough—Lorrie's cheeks paling, her friends frozen into the dismayed stillness of the interrupted masturbator—I am not too sure about the graceful side of our exit. . . .

Jim now opens his eyes and throws his arms around me, repeating over and over that he is pleased with me. We talked at length last night, between uncomplicated surges of passion. Our deeds are still with us, as a surrounding haze, thicker and thicker, moving us to succumb again, but at the same time we hunger for a stringent hot bath and a long unreasonable breakfast. Those last two urges win. Master and slave share the tub, and soap each other just short of forgetting about food.

It is Jim's idea to go back to Lorrie's place. He tells me he found a call from her on our way to the coffee shop, at the hotel desk.

An hour later, I have been turned over one of Lorrie's chairs, of wine-red velveteen, on which my mouth foams away gratifying pain. Jim makes me count every stroke of the paddle, of the cat, in a clear loud voice. He applies them knowingly, never hitting the same spot twice in a row, reddening my whole rear progressively and pulling my head back, my eyes lowered under his stare. Then he rubs the fire away and kisses my hot flesh. Up again goes the whip, and my body cringes, expecting another lash, but it is only the caress of air, fanned around, liquid and cool to my hips, by the bittersweet-smelling leather snake.

Lorrie has closed herself in her room with Gene, after a few chilly words and a sarcastic invitation, flaunted out as a dare, to make ourselves at home. After she has slammed the door shut, Jim pushes my clothes up gently and parts with the real reason he brought me here: he wants to shame Lorrie, who had agreed with him in advance that she would not take any cut out of my fee. Impatient to say good-by to Lorrie's greed and histrionics, he says that he holds no final grudge against her because she made it possible for him, a week ago, to hear Gene Davis and Douglas Brandt rave about "Spread-Eagle Upside-Down Lily." (This depicts one of the fantasies I am not eager to act out, but I have found it a most handy bedtime tale as a background to onanism for would-be sadists.)

"Freak-off Doug," alias Douglas Brandt, of Brandt,

Goldmann, & Katz Co., was the first man to take a hair-brush to my bottom. He delivered me to the diamond-ringed hands of "Tommy the Toad," and a young cherubic follower of his, Hans, a student in genetics from Hamburg. As a team, that loving pair launched me through the initial whipping session that provided my twenty-five-year-old obsessive wish with the kind of excessive experience no beginner in the arts of chastisement should ever be exposed to: I was gagged, chained, assaulted with a huge dildo, abused, slapped and flogged spiritedly, left with marks that kept my bed partners guessing for three weeks. That was the time I played truant with the calendar, selecting Tuesday, Wednesday, and Thursday nights for my orgiastic sprees and farfetched alibis. (The three-days-in-a-row policy kept me from sobering up.) My days were spent teaching art in a Bronx college, keeping a disorganized, chaotic house for the Professor, my husband, and saving my heart, awkward and divided as it was, for the young son I helped him father.

As I leave Lorrie's place with Jim, I cannot help laughing in Gene's face when he escorts us to the door, looking at me murderously over a few sections of the Sunday *Times*, the dog box he is being sent out to clean, and a half-empty bottle of vodka. Behind the closed door, we hear a crash and shriek and we run down the stairs, laughing like fully baked idiots.

We return to the Hilton, where Jim nurses the rosy highlights on my back. He fetches the ointment himself, and, crooning endearments, eases the pain off the welts that decorate my flesh, all the while cursing the brute who mishandled me so. Then he sits by the phone and orders a couple of steaks: a matching medium-rare.

In bed, there will be no play tonight, but my solemn

introduction to the LSD ritual. Jim used to be an alco-
holic. He is now a psychedelic-wise ex-lush. The "brew,"
as he calls it, also helps him keep away from the whip for
long periods. He thinks it would be bliss to put to death,
once and for all, that craving for pain, that madness that
brought us togther and held us in its embrace. Yes, even
though we can be swept away by such a surging, seething
arson, we still can name the fault in us that keeps us
going back for more burns.

Twenty minutes after munching on that innocent-look-
ing sugar cube, I start feeling very conscious of my
smeared make-up. There is something definitely fishy
about Jim's refusing to let me go to the bathroom to
freshen up. What is there in the bathroom I am not supposed to see? I imagine my own reflection in the mirror,
preceding me, waiting for me. Is Jim unwilling to stay
alone for a few minutes? The thought that he might be
frightened makes me taste my own fear so abjectly that
nothing now would make me get up from this bed and
walk to the john. At the same time I want to go to the
bathroom badly. To the desire of looking at myself in the
mirror is added the certainty that I am turning into a
witch. I can feel the skin on my face dry up and hang
loose, hair grow on it in tufts. I must endure both the
horror of turning into a monster and the paralyzing anguish that keeps me from walking to the mirror to make
sure.

Seen from very close, Jim's face swells and reddens, his
nose grows bigger and crooked at the end. His mouth
widens and drops at the corners. He looks like Tommy
the Toad, who advised me to turn my hobby, fornicating,
into a profitable venture, pointing out to me that I was
already spending on my back every minute I managed to

15

steal from family life. Tommy's beauty marks start popping on Jim's chin, and I hide my eyes, shaking. Two arms rescue me tightly, and Jim's voice is there to remind me that even with the panic and the shock, room 2814 is still sheltering us. I ask to see the key. You never know with somebody who looks like Tommy the Toad.

Jim goes on talking reassuringly, turning away from me with my father's profile, and I feel like answering: "Yes, Sir." I can see in his troubled eyes that I also look like many of his women, from the first little girl he fondled behind a fence, to his baby girl of today, the one he calls "cream puff." I try to ignore the threatening shape lurking by the windows, half-hidden by the drapes. A cold wind invades me, rattling me like a dead tree. I become dry leaves and wood to be burned. Jim repeats stubbornly: "You're beautiful, Lily." The way he looks, it's hard to believe him. Suddenly his face becomes a broken mirror, then a pool of stagnant water, and I can contemplate the ghoulish features I have been hiding from myself all my life. I start laughing and trembling at the same time in an ugly teeth-chattering fit of mirth. Jim tries to control me but we are the two tormented parts of the same worm and he ends up joining me.

I finally turn my back on him, ignoring his pleas. I whisper some of the verses I treasure the most, from Alfred de Musset's "Les Nuits":

> Le mal dont j'ai souffert s'est enfui comme un rêve.
> Je n'en peux comparer le lointain souvenir
> Qu'à ces brouillards légers que l'aurore soulève
> Et qu'avec la rosée on voit s'évanouir.

My voice becomes a beautifully mastered mezzo echoing through a cave of sounds awakened by my call. I plunge deep into the incommunicable. I share the poet's insight, aware of what he chose to express, what he could not penetrate, and what he wished to leave unsaid. I am the Word and the Sound that silence all music. The cave explodes and shoots up in a million stars, my voice rising higher, then dissolving into stillness. Those tired, empty, bombastic words show me their hollow, delusive shell at first, but as I let them sink into the new light, as I slowly repeat them, they come alive, vibrant and full of the substance they were once mocking and faking. Jim's wail reaches me from down below, dulling the lights one by one. "Lily, come back!" When he pulls at my shoulder I fall back from a great height. My breath comes in gasps. My head swirls. As I look into Jim's eyes, I see he also had his own kingdom to rule for a second of abolished time. He was the part in me that heard his voice, as I was in him the memory of a name. We do not have to explain to each other where we were and what we left, to sink back to that diminished, opaque world of the blind.

We wake up, star dust clinging to our fingers derisively, as befits any trip beyond us, so much beyond us. And together, moved perhaps by a sense of wonder, a respect for the sacred, we will talk willingly about the anxious moments of our journey, the unfamiliarity and the chaos of it, but me will not unveil any of the revelation that was foisted upon us in equal shares. What one has seen, the other has seen also. Our eyes meet, and that is enough. I think of that closing line in my history book about the religious beliefs of the ancient Romans: "The priests could not look at each other straight in the eye without laughing."

17

We fall asleep like the wounded, and wake up late next morning, two refreshed pilgrims, elated and lucid to each other, with no need for sex or violence.

Jim goes back to Philadelphia, to his blonde, Presbyterian, hypochondriac, green-fingered wife, their two young daughters, and the unexotic intricacies of the insurance business. He leaves me with a fat roll of bills "for cab fare" wrapped up in my breakfast napkin. I was with him all day yesterday and he heard me check on the phone with my answering service where calls piled up. I belong with his world, outside of any professional antics. I shall be a thing, pliant and handy under his touch, not a product his wallet can alienate. I worship his God-sent knack for releasing my inner devils, through an ever vulnerable peace treaty. Because of that insane compulsion that drives me to abuse and exhaust my body for money, I guess that Jim, who has paid for my services for the first and last time, may become a luxury in my life. Now and then, I will punish myself into deciding that I cannot afford him and all the wear and tear our games will occasionally bring to my emotions. But this man pushed me back into the line of marching hostages where I had my place reserved from the beginning of my years. The pretexts I will give myself in the future for fighting his imperious calling of my name will do no more than space our meetings; they shall recur as inevitably as rainfall, all the more merciless after a storm has been delayed.

He tells me to let him know if Lorrie "tries anything out of line." He begs me not to take more chances than I must, in a way of life oh, so precarious, which, he repeats, I have chosen as a short cut to self-hate, more deadly than the whipping sessions I still must have as frosting on my cake (humble pie), or the only cherry left on top.

We both love breakfast at the Automat. We eat nearly everything in sight: oatmeal with three helpings of cream, strawberries, French toast and bacon, ice cream, juice, and coffee. Over that bountiful ammunition, we exchange our first private jokes. With Jim, I will learn later, it will always be the same pace: the jump in the fire, the step back, the parting of ways.

2

January 6th

After Jim has gone, I walk under a lowering cloud of unreality. All routines are distorted. My weekly trips to the bank vault leave me cold. Business slows down from lack of new contacts, and it does not bother me. I try to keep in touch with the peace Jim left with me, but it is fading already. Our phone talk pushes us farther apart as it makes my longing sharper, and I resent it. I play at night with the whips he bought me. I coil them around my neck, my thighs. I antagonize the few Johns I know who are subtle enough to notice it, but they miss the cue every time and my temper swells high and stays there, a victim of priapism.

I could go to see Russell Green, the jolly bald horse-whipper who used to attend to me under the Toad's orders; he would help me to wait for Jim's return. But after the moving subtleties I have just been broken in to and spared with, Russell's monotonous riding-club techniques will be too much of a disappointment. Better shoot with blanks than miss.

When I discuss those two days at length with Cass,

some weekend over lunch, every relinquished word, every described gesture turns to dust, and ends up on the comical side. Emotions then felt so vividly regain as little of their brilliance as the stare of a stuffed animal. My good sense, alive and kicking too late, rebels at admitting the delights found in rehearsed humiliation. The pride I threw down so zestfully at Jim's feet is getting up, counting its missing feathers. Cass laughs at my efforts to rationalize what happened and, munching on an apple as he lies on my bumpy couch, his collegy, white-socked feet up on the table between the Chianti bottle and a pile of chicken bones, he reminds me tolerantly that whatever I may feel like the morning after, I must never be regretful of my curiosity at experimenting with emotions, as long as I remain able to control them. Now that I have cooled down, out of necessity, the memory of certain excesses and the circumstances of my masochistic surrender may seem to me objectionable and grotesque. But I must not forget that any act of passion, considered apart from its motivation, looks equally laughable, even the so-called normal acts.

Cass, the only young broker to reach Wall Street every morning on a scooter, his black tie flying out to the side, his vest buttoned high, his beautiful Eurasian face impavid, always looks his best—and his worst would be enough for the most fastidious onlooker—when he buries himself in abstraction. It makes him seem all the more real and earthy, especially when biting on an apple. I try to draw my first charcoal study for a portrait of him, as he questions me on my LSD session and Jim's connection with the two now infamous professors who fathered the drug's career. I then indulge in some research work on my own, kissing away from Cass's chin a fat shiny apple pit. What follows might have Newton's approval, from a strictly technical point of view. The old reflexes are still good, and we mix with their actual fitness some invigorating recollections of our freshly maturing past, from the wild, improbable scene of our first meeting to a number of common exposures to the most swinging circles that make New York so arrestingly un-American.

After I have washed the dishes it is dark, and I turn on the lamp. Cass finishes reading the paper's business section and reminds me to go to see that agent who promised to find me another apartment downtown. He adds that I have been lucky so far that the cardboard warehouse next door has not been introduced to a lighted match, that the thin rusty fence over my window did not meet with a cutting blade—no worth-while raping could be expected from that part of Greenwich Village, anyhow —that my pocketbook did not pass from under my arm to the paw of a night prowler, as I stand on deserted Charles Street waiting for a cab, on my way to a late-late job.

I admit he is right, and I list the fire-hazard warehouse as my number one headache. I do not welcome the prospect of greeting the summer from this unholy manger, after being cornered and closed in and snowed under and sooted around and through for a whole winter, with nothing to watch from my window but my neighbors' unwashed feet.

Cass leaves after throwing three pailfuls of hot soapy water at my windows, from the outside. The fence retains the suds, the glass panes cling to the steam. I kiss him and button up his duffle coat as he looks down at me, all smiling-sphinx. He puts on his dopey sunglasses, intent on resting his eyes from the contact lenses he insists on wearing at work during the week, despite the rubbing on his tight fishes. Twenty-seven years ago, in the Middle West, a small, bashful Japanese bookbinder married a blonde, buoyant Russian-born circus rider. The same good fairies who once gathered around Sleeping Beauty's cradle set forth for their second trip—the first one turned out too much of a failure to remain unchallenged in history—to celebrate Cass's coming into the world. To this day, they are still overpampering him with special up-to-date privileges, and their solicitude is forever saving him by the bell.

I like to feed him on Sundays and send him out in the cold to his next date. It is Sheil tonight. I am just starting to approve of her. On the doorstep, he asks me how satisfied I am with Mightyjoe, a health-club encounter of his, whom he brought to me last week in a doting attempt to regain both my hide and mind, trapped in faraway Philadelphia. Besides, Cass shows interest in Connie, Mightyjoe's estranged green-eyed wife. After suffering for a short while from Connie's cuddly attacks on his lowest boiling point, Cass found a way to lend back to his pal, with the left hand, what he was planning to borrow from him, using both hands. Mightyjoe does gratify my weakness for hard-rippling muscles and tender nearsighted blundering eyes. I find that mixture irresistible. Oh, the erotic fluttering in my loins when my bespectacled men part with their glasses, unwrap their eyeballs with the merest twinkle of a bump and grind, and stare at me with a naked, bewildered look that always leaves me the benefit of the doubt, as they must now operate strictly on poetic memory. . . . I am nearsighted too, and the winks I exchange with myself in the mirror do nothing to alter my mistrust of the vulgarity of twenty-twenty vision that holds back no mystery, necessitates no ritual.

Learn to be ecstatic about your faults, and your ugliest virtues will not carry you away. Away is where you do not belong.

Mightyjoe, this young ball of synthetic fire, happens to be too demanding on my time (blissfully ignorant of my profession as he is), and knocks me out too much in the sack, which deteriorates my gusto at business. But I must admit he is one out of a thousand in that body-building club where, along with Cass, he has been exercising, swimming, lifting weights, and discouraging amorous pansies for the past year. His narrow hips, his drum-taut belly carry their heavy fruit like a trophy. I love to see under a lean, spare middle such a lavish, munificent bunch of male organs.

But Mightyjoe is not vain. He does not take much comfort in the size of his endowments. In his sweet, weak eyes, they will never compensate for a homely pock-marked face that could be just West-Side Jewish, but goes all overboard Riverside-Drive-Yiddish-camp. He tries a little too hard to inflict his hobbies on me and his mania for capital letters, which he mouths away as if he were nibbling on the holy Host. Unflinchingly antique-oriented, he bores me very quickly with his heated soliloquies about Early American subtleties, hypersensuous overtones of the Baroque Age, and the superfluity of the neo-Grecian. All over Tenth Street bookstalls, he hunts obscure magazines filled with the blotchy woodcuts of some café society illustrator of 1903. To top it all, that unpolished rooster dares to be jealous of Cass, which I will not tolerate long. I suppose a third-rate understudy cannot help feeling that way about a "grand premier role," but the uncouth thing to do is to voice it. And to end the relationship, I will not wait for my tea leaves to show me the gleam of a Bavarian game knife between Cass's shoulder blades. So till the day when I say adieu, I will go on extricating myself from under Mightyjoe, even when he still shows signs of acute devotion that might lead him to better my score and start working on his own. He ends up feeling like a pig and apologizes. This pre-occupation of mine with speed and the need to aggravate my partner keeps us on a run-around, from the Olde Shoppes on Bleecker and Perry streets, to the exhibit rooms of furniture d'époque at the Metropolitan Museum and the silent movie program at the Modern Art, back to my bedsprings, no allowances made for the dates I break for business necessity, gossiping sessions and time out with Cass, work at my easel, and the frequent need to be alone.

Cass has become very dear to me. I cannot stand to hear a derogatory word said about him unless I have thought it up first and presented it to his grudging appreciation. We are accomplices, brothers under the skin, at times fiendish friends. I almost spoiled the tribal game by insisting that we have a romance first. Cass waited, not unkindly, till I thought better of it.

We had met, one crusty-soft, porous spring night, across the street from an East-Side apartment house which I was hesitating to enter. It was going to be another party. . . . I had heard all the jokes of the season.

It might have never happened. I shall recall and celebrate it, write it on matchbook covers, used envelopes, ladies-room doors, and my left thumbnail.

From a small Italian restaurant I had, half an hour earlier, called Cobby Leash, the host. His drilling voice had forced me to hold the receiver two inches away from my ear.

"Funnybunny it's you, thank God! The party is creeping up to the highest expectations; I can count (I can still count) sixteen nice human beings, eleven of whom, or which, or whose, are three-legged. . . ."

I interrupted him: "You don't even make sense when you're sober, Cobbs. Now listen: remember I told you I couldn't make it tonight because I was having dinner with the Badrianopopoulos? Well, I showed up too late, or I had the wrong checkered-tableclothed side of the street. Anyhow. . . ."

He boomed again: "Wonnerful. You join us right away, Yummy one."

I had one point to clear up: "Wait a minute, Cob. Is Pedro there? I don't want to smell that greasy fried egg again. He's going to slit his throat once more and I've taken about all I. . . ."

But Cob would see to that: "Please honey, come up. I'll handle Pedro. I'll fix everything. I told him you wouldn't show up, and he'll leave soon. In any case I promise there'll be no trouble this time. All the windows are stuck; I saw to it."

We were disconnected. I scratched the number around furiously. Three times, the line was busy. I could not go back home to Paleface, my spouse, who was no doubt sprawled on the sofa, wringing his hands in front of the early show. I needed a third Scotch and a fourth. Cobby's crowd would do. Chasing after the Badrianopopoulos all over the Greek and Turkish nightspots would be tiresome. I got into a cab, planning to drink just enough so that the damage caused to Pedro would not show. Here was the story: a common little Spanish featherweight was losing his eyesight; sad. He had taken me too seriously, which I had warned him not to do. His own fault. Because I stopped calling him "lambie," he threatened to jump through the window. I said: "Do it." He started to oblige. Cob, our host and referee, twice as big and tall, grabbed him almost not in time. End of story.

I walked right into Pedro that night; two lean young men were following him, watching over his intoxicated condition. One of them was Cass. We looked at each other and started wondering where we had met before. We never stopped wondering.

After introducing himself as Eliot Kerr, the third fellow took advantage of that distinct fluttering of wings and speedily piled us all in his car, explaining that the party upstairs was moving to his place, on the West Side. Even Pedro could not irk me during the ride, though he tried by embracing me, holding my chin, and hugging my knees. I kept my eyes glued to Cass's profile, and, shyly turning to me, he would smile back, glance at Pedro, and crinkle his perfect nose. (Pedro was ugly in a grand manner, except for what he kept packed in his old-fashioned underpants.)

Cobby and a few of his men friends joined us later in Eliot's roomy flat. Cass's nearness turned me on so high and burning that at least one man out of three benefited from the glow. As I was the only girl there, it left Cass much flabbergasted. He was lying, brown and spicy, close

to me, on the feather-littered rug—one pillow had ex-
ploded under me—in the middle of a circle of naked men.
Pedro was in the kitchen, dead drunk thanks to Cobby. I
never saw anybody from that crowd again. They had
played their part: they had brought Cass to me.

I was to learn, much later, from Sheil, that Cass left
that night dazed and shocked more than a little by my
availability. The immediately reactionary part of him,
which delighted at triumphing over a girl's resistance,
considered me the most promiscuous specimen of "femal-
ity" that he had ever stumbled on, with not a puff of
breath wasted on courting and wooing.

On another, far-seeing level, he quickly evaluated the
sweeping experiences he could expect from his introduction to my world. So he gave me his card and I called
him a week later, curious to check on my memories of his
boyish beauty and aloofness. That we became uncom-
fortably fond of each other over the months that followed
still amazes me because of the handicap inflicted on our
emotions by the knowledge that Cass never had to win
me over in the least, and that if the choice had been fully
his, he might have hesitated to bring to his bed that de-
vouring black widow he could not help visualize as a
threat. My lust for conquest struck him as a virile attribute, which he cruelly underlined at the precise times I
was melting for him in passive and tender fashion.

My creative gifts bemused and stirred him to an ambivalent jealous delectation. For a long time, I never tried
to use any pins and needles on his sorest points: those
Oriental looks that made him so exotic and appealing but
decidedly different, which he flinched at, as a sixth-grader
would; his social awkwardness that plunged him into fits

29

of muteness; his petty handling of money. The last two traits were very like my own faults, as I am a capricious social animal myself and obsessed by the horror of having to spend my pennies by the hundreds. Yes, I would refrain from pointing out to Cass his less commendable peculiarities, and stoically let his comments on my own faults pile over.

He would say, in mild bewilderment: "You know, most of my friends consider you quite attractive!"

Or: "I cannot see why you sweat so much."

Close to him, in those days, I felt in such an agony of organic anxiety that I would indeed be drenched with perspiration. He gave me gas pains just by lifting his eyebrows and I was so busy experiencing rapture in his embrace that I never could relax. The day when I passed wind quite richly in his presence, I yearned for instant death and cremation. My cupful of tormented lenity ran over when Cass told me once, while slinking away from bed, after I had dared utter some slightly more committed endearment than I usually ventured: "Lots of girls are crazy about me at the moment. I don't let it disturb me." The ceiling did not fall. On the contrary, it snapped right back where it belonged: above my head.

On Cass's arm I once entered a rambling, mice-infested barn inhabited by Dave Bernheim, a photographer friend of Cass, his old groggy, melancholic dog, and an odd dozen tropical fish. Mary-Ann Lebas, one of Cass's transient girls at the time, was clinging to his other arm. She clinged—clung—too hard and was left holding nothing. Cass wanted me to see Dave's collection of challenging photographs; rosy entwined private parts in full gear, acts of fraternization with the animal world, and précis drawings relating the extrascholastic activities of a teenage vice club busted the previous year, "on the outskirts of town"—just like that beautiful, unfair blues sung by Ray Charles. Detailed sketches induced that particular precinct's Finest into adorning their conjugal duties for a while with a few flourishes. The whole file was submitted to wide circulation throughout the Force, and was lent and borrowed for a fee, like a library book, before ending its traveling career in Dave's appreciative hands. The most curious electrical device of them all, tailed by a rolling, jerking, vibrating handle, was also relocated by Dave, who stored it lovingly. It was no doubt fitted to the dimensions of the average bad high-school girl, and Sheil and I were much impressed to discover that we were doing all right by it, during sessions of group therapy that reunited us frequently with Cass and Dave at the studio.

Cass pushes me to paint and write, set my hair once in a while, and not fall in love. His criticism, his advice are sharp and sensible, at various levels.

"You have been using a lot of the same color, recently. That sickly red. . . ."

"When are you going to start writing something good for a change, instead of talking aloud over toilet paper?"

"The way your hair is getting thin on the sides, you should cut it to give it body, or let it grow longer and pin it high, or wear a wig or something."

"You mean you paid twenty-five dollars and seventy-two cents for just one bedspread?"

"Where is your telephone bill from last month? In the sugar bowl or under the Tampax box?"

"So you don't know any better than using that medieval douche bag . . . Jesus Christ. . . . There's not a schoolgirl

31

in Ohio who hasn't heard about that new thing without a pipe that you fill right at the faucet, then you take hold of your. . . ."

"Why don't you send your son one of those chemistry sets instead of burying him under more and more brain-shrinking comic books? You want him to grow up as sick as your Johns' kids?"

"What time have you been getting out of bed all week? Eleven o'clock? Fine. . . . This painting should be finished the week before Christmas, with luck."

"What are you trying to prove with those off-black stockings, your legs are dirty or something? Maybe your better half is going into mourning for the other."

He comes to me with problems too:

"You got to talk to Sheil and make her stop shooting her mouth off about me."

"I want you to meet Susan. She can't wait to spit on you. She's been looking at your paintings on my wall and hearing all about your intellect."

"Do I look better in my camel's-hair coat than in my black top with the velvet collar?"

"Don't tell Sheil I called you to tell you she called."

"Do you think my place looks awful? Last night I took a girl in there, and I saw her face fall. Maybe I should invest in a second-hand rug?"

"Can I send you stocks in my sister's name?"

"You've got to come to that party with me. I must bring a girl. I won't let anybody bother you. You can even *sleep* there if you are tired. You don't have to do a thing."

"Do you have the number of that freak Sheil laid at Roy's last week? He told her about the Armenian girl who was in *Playboy* twice this winter. Sheil hasn't seen him again, but you could ask Saul. . . ."

"Please drop my name when you see Mister Clean. He promised he would let me know about Gloria's friend, Deborah. She used to answer the phone for him."

"If you meet Debbie at Roy's tell her I left for Michigan."

"What do you think a girl means when she tells you she would just as well have a hamburger as a steak and walk around the park as see a show?"

"Susan is talking a lot about getting engaged. I don't know what to do. Maybe I should introduce her to Mightyjoe, if you can spare him."

"Why can't girls take sex as I do?"

He directed me in the acquisition of a safe-deposit box at the bank, and saw to it that I had a post-office box as well. It took some doing and I remember a whole morning of phone calls.

"Cass, I am at the post office. They say they want my home address."

"Cass, I am on my way to the bank. What did you say I should ask for and whom?"

"Cass, I am just back from the vault. Should I have given them my real name? Why is everybody so nosey?"

I introduced Cass to *Atone in Tune,* the S. and M. paper, printed in Toronto, that Jim was forwarding to me every week. We carefully scanned the ads. Some were from "breathers"—the new word for swingers—not looking for discipline-seekers but for "broad-minded congenial fun-loving singles and couples." Cass put an ad in himself and had me hysterical at the way he worded it:

Extremely attractive, sophisticated, intelligent, curious-minded, refined, cultured, well-spoken, widely traveled and read, college-graduated successful young executive would like to meet attractive women or couples.

What bothered Cass was the limitation imposed upon the advertiser. He felt deeply unsatisfied at leaving so much unsaid. When, after a decent amount of time, it was plain that no one was going to answer that ad, I offered the comment that maybe no readers were ready yet for such perfection.

3

February 2nd

Cass thought I was losing my mind when I settled down at the end of September in that out-of-the-way, dark, tiny basement room on Carpenter Street. He stared at the peeling gray paint, the littered broken steps leading down to the door, the punched-in metal fence, the sooty windows. When I had been paraded through there earlier in the week by the agency's barker, after stating, in the Eighth Street office, that I wanted just one room, cheap but nice, as soon as possible, the air had been crisp, flavored with wood smoke, wet suede, and my own eager infantilism. Carpenter Street under the morning sun had not looked a bit tacky, the sidewalks alive with candy-wrappers, no trucks or garbage cans around because it happened to be the week when both sanitation and packaging were on strike. I had okayed the place and signed the lease right away. Now, with the sun gone, the warehouse booming, and the garbage piled high in and out of cans, it looked worse than one of those Cunard Line shipyard backstreets.

I did not have much of a choice. I had to get out of my

boy's room—now empty—in my husband's apartment up in Washington Heights. He allowed me to sleep there, as long as I kept out of his sight, till he moved out himself; out of a home we had shared for seven years, out of that city he had always hated, out of that country he made responsible for all the sins of the world, including mine. But I could not sleep on my son's cot spotted with modeling clay, surrounded by scribbled walls, soft toys, space outfits, Superman comic books and last year's homework casualties: peanut-butter-sticky notes that read, "Alan stinks more than Freddie," and "The teacher is on parole." My husband had not let me pack all the toys. He promised Michel he would buy him everything new at home, but I had cheated and stuffed the child's suitcases with all I could salvage of his most prized possessions. I refused to think that he would not be allowed to keep them at the boarding school.

So, on Carpenter Street, I told Cass firmly: "I will move out when I can afford something better. Don't tell me that kind of lease is hard to break." Back from France, where I had left my son, I did not own anything here but a cloggy sinus, loads of paintings that would not sell—my own—and ninety-two dollars. I was starting my trade from scratch after my not quite unsuccessful attempts of the past years to detect in myself an incurable case of nymphomania. I had finally worn out my husband's patience and exasperating kindness and lost the right to bring up my son. Now, that not entirely faked-out ailment of mine had better pay off, since I would have to be my own breadwinner, for the first time in my life.

My "cellar" felt cozy from the start. "Your place looks better than mine!" Cass was puzzled, his eyes on the fire-

36

place and shelves, heavy with books. My paintings hid the cracked whitewashed walls, and I made the most of the kitchenette by hiding it with an extra blanket that had to be brought down to keep Cass warm whenever he stayed overnight. I was paying the unlikely rent of ninety-five dollars a month. Too much for that punch bowl of a room. I discovered I could paint only from early morning to budding noon. It was all right, after a fair night's sleep, to ascend from bed, at around quarter to eight, and grope for a warm coat, a comb for my gnarly mane, a cup of tea, and my paintbrushes. (The coat first. . . . The radiator started to hiss and puff away balmy steam at about eleven.) But when the calls of the berth made me keep late hours, I would be still stupefied with sleep at the time daylight would vanish from my crater, turning it into a dubious Rembrandt background.

Then I started breaking things. The furniture was already at the point of collapse, and I soon came up with the tiny amount of pushing it needed to finish the job. One lampshade of waxed cardboard popped up. Temper. The folding table lost two legs. I would still be able to use it, by sticking one detached limb between the floor and the tabletop, after opening one side. But I kick once in a while when I draw, and I upset the inkbottle over a couple of almost finished drawings. I had two captain's chairs held together with string in the back. They fell apart after a small portion of petting. I pulled all the sticks out: they love me, they love me not, they love me. I had to leave one stick in the middle, it would not come off. It rose on the transformed stool like a healthy phallus: what a terrific answer from the daisy. . . .

The rug was a dull wine-colored, threadbare piece of

nonsense. I did not stain it much with paint because nothing showed on it. In my cot, a spring jumped up every ten minutes or so, right between my shoulder blades. It was a question of good timing in order to fall asleep. The windows had new yellow rayon curtains that partly melted in the first wash. Ironing stuck the material together, but it remained sheer. The blinds were in good shape when I moved in, but the left one refused to go down a month later. . . . As it grew very hot by evening, I would not be wearing much, and an occasional knock and cheer at the left window would recall me to the barest two-piece modesty.

I once phoned the landlord's office to expose the case of my capricious radiator, and I was reminded that one had to give up a few bourgeois commodities for the privilege of becoming a Villager. The landlord lives on Park Avenue at the right latitude.

When my room grew dark, I would strain my eyes for half an hour, then put my paintbox away, push my easel back in the window corner, scrub my fingers, take a bath, fluff my hair, eat a sandwich, make the bed, empty the ashtrays, grab the floral spray and turn it loose, clean the bathroom, and be ready for John number one.

They fell for the Bohemian bit. They drove down to Carpenter Street in their big cars for a touch of slumming with a former university wife, recent college instructor, who, disturbingly often, spoke better English than they did and had read all the books piled high in her rathole. After they got their heavy breathing taken care of, many would indulge in some analyzing:

"How could your husband ever let you go?"

"What a waste . . . a woman like you. . . ."

"Did your parents reject you when you were a child?"

And I would turn the radio on loud if it lasted more than the five self-revaluating minutes they were entitled to, in their attempt to dissociate their puzzlement over my hidden self from their enjoyment of my obvious one. They kept coming back.

The phone is close to my easel; most men call in the late morning and all I have to do is put my brush down and answer.

"What are you doing, honeybun? Stretching your gorgeous legs and rubbing your sleepy eyes?"

Why don't I ever answer, "No, I'm counting my crabs"?

Cass introduced me to a Belgian-born Lesbian who owns a small gallery on Cobble Street. She sells Mexican beads, arty Christmas cards, pottery ashtrays, and, once in a drastic while, a drawing. Cass advised me to leave my door open. She walked in, strong-jawed and wiry. I said quickly: "It's very hot. You won't mind the draft?" She did not flinch. She once fought with Cass over a blonde, but they made up and she now holds him in good-natured contempt. She was pleasant, her aggressiveness well controlled, her pants sharply creased. She saw in my drawings ". . . a streak of rebellion against the set patterns of morality." And I nodded eagerly over my glass of rosé wine, my face thickly buttered by the stupidity that washes over me when my art work is praised or defiled or joked at. I merely want to be ignored. It gives me all latitude to exercise complacent self-appraisal. She took eleven of my pen-and-ink drawings and did not sell a single one.

I was through peddling around the best and the worst art galleries, as I had been doing the previous years, with not much method. I had picked, on purpose, the most prestigious places, where only big names could enter, those of solid repute where my fumbling would provoke negative smiles, and the dumpiest art-groceries eager to store almost anything in their back rooms. To avoid displeasing those friends who would go to great lengths to force me out of obscurity, I obliged with a few trips to the galleries where I had been personally recommended, expressing mealy-mouthed gratitude, but hugging to my deceitful bosom the charisma of idolized failure, my goal. I was invariably relieved by rejection.

Where was the little girl whom Picasso had wished to meet, seventeen years ago, after glancing at her sketches? That precocious brat's leftovers now shaped up a fetchy dish for some art-loving Bronx contractor. I would be faithful only to my barest sense of worth, saving part of my time to revive part of my pride, managing to produce one or two canvases a month—for I paint slowly, with the Primitives' care for details—.

I hated it when Johns would look at my work, or go as far as rave about it and even ask if "that little still life down there was for sale." They made my paintings dirty just by looking at them. I would answer evasively and start unknotting their ties. Cass quarreled with me about what he called my "pigheadedness." He said that practically nobody buys paintings except Johns.

"Show me a private collector, I'll show you a John."

"Maybe so, Cass, but I will not let the same wallet that financed its way between my sheets follow the same path up to my easel's top. I might sell my work to somebody else's John. Not mine."

The only John who could make me talk about my work and even ask him for advice was Mikael Parnonsky, an old Polish painter shipped to me by the character Cass, Sheil, and I call Mister Clean, alias Saul Cohenz, tentative owner of a well-located art gallery which is not paid for yet, I assume, because when Saul lets you have cab fare, if he cannot persuade anybody to drive you home, he goes through all his tight-fitting pockets like mad, and you end up with three quarters, six dimes, and eleven nickels. . . . Unless he manages to remember where his brothers Seymour parked his car, an ancient Mercedes with red cushions full of hairpins and ether flasks.

Saul is in the illimited fifties, wears a bushy gray mustache—because you must sport hair somewhere— holds his anxious, compact, sprightly body very erect, so as not to lose one half-inch out of the four stretched ones he tops his five feet with, speaks in the Donald-Duck way of one who pulls in his stomach for hours at a time, dresses Flamboyant Florida, for the sake also of the letter F, is touchy about his aging looks, and needs to be patted forever on the back. You get a sore arm doing that, as well as an ear very much bent at his Casanovian tall tales. He uses his women to close his selling deals; he uses his selling deals to renew his supply of women.

His taste in sex runs to the anal-exotic. He always made me keep on my high heels and black stockings, held with his own fetish garter belt: a stringful of fringes, red pompons, and velvet bows which turned me into one of those fancy horses that trot around Central Park. Crouching on all fours, I watched, upside down, from between my thighs, a mischievous little faun stepping out of satin robes and, legs well apart, fondling a raised penis with both his hands, all the while talking to my very moist and ready rear end.

I got tired of his continual demand for "creative sex-talk." I drove him crazy once by describing unhurriedly what I wished he could do to me in the subway, at rush hour. Ever since, he expects some new elaborate fantasy; and while it pleased me to evoke a mood, a spell, at my leisure, I was repelled by the senility it produced in him.

Through Saul, I became one of Big Pappy Phil Mac-Moose's guests at those fabulous hard-to-crash candlelit scenes Cardinal Spellman was never invited to. It was well worth bearing with Saul.

Mikael Parnonsky had a show at Saul's gallery. He mixed his own colors, starting with raw powders, and used, instead of the common finishing varnish, a blend of clear glue, liquid virgin wax, and a mysterious third element that gave a glassy texture to his oils. The colors seemed to be oven-cooked. Aside from that, he was an old dear. He had come to see me once before his show opened and had left crimson-red and satisfied by my bed-side *delicatesse*. He was a poor, worn-out solitaire player. I was then battling with a painting which threatened to remain unfinished. It was a tall, standing nude. My state of grace was taking leave, it was becoming too arduous. A nude must be painted in joy and buoyancy, emanating from the paint itself, if not from the painter. Mikael loved the flesh tone, the masklike face, the raised arm gloved in green. Cass thought it a bit weird, but invigorating; it was his first positive critical statement for a long time and to show him my enthusiasm I took him to the opening of Mikael's show, as ever a treat for me to be seen with Cass, for us both to share jokes over Saul's bald pate, and a golden opportunity for my escort to collect new girls' phone numbers: the Cohenz gallery is used by itinerant party-goers and crashers as a pause on the way to a sex scene.

42

It was a day of national disaster that held New York transfixed by shock and loss. The opening had to be a flop, even for Cass who met only aging emaciated girls rolled in furs and discarded by the Peace Corps itself. The crowd was thin and quite a bit older than I expected from previous openings, mournful and little concerned with art. But for three hours old Mika went on being the soul of Continentalism, kissing hands, showing his badly capped teeth, pulling his pocket watch, bowing from the waist with a discreet creaking of bones that made me feel guilty. He eventually had to be carried to the office's armchair, and I promised myself to turn him down if he was foolish enough to call on me again with more than shoptalk on his mind. Saul was hugging everything in skirts to show everything in pants what was his score of the year. He had the poor tan of the destitute snob who cannot afford a whole weekend in the sun. He explained it by stating that he hardly had time to come up for air, what with a pile of Bahama girls over him and all.

Electrified by the threat of Cass on the loose in his lair, he was dancing and mincing and winking around like a maniac, reflecting neon flashes on his shiny scalp, embracing and petting the men with the exuberance of the latent pansy and congratulating himself, aloud, for being surrounded, as ever, by so many "beautiful people." Saul was referring to those gifted with the cunning deviousness, supple spine, numerous informers and contacts that establish a good "breathing" reputation. The right jargon helps, too: you must know when, where, in front of whom, and with which implements, "to turn a new chick on." You only bother with people you "relate to." No female, no matter how "crazy," can ever "threaten you with her cunt." You teach your women to "watch out for the users," and you make it your personal altruistic business to see that they are "serviced" by your friends in exchange for the same favors from said friends who share the same humanitarianism. The outsiders are the taboo-filled "squares who don't know from nothing" and cannot "dig a scene." It is a small world, and at times you must exercise caution: you may associate with a fellow for a whole half-month, before finding out "he is groovy too." I cannot overcome my amazement at hearing grown men, many of them past their prime, express themselves like yesterday's teenagers.

Mister Clean's own speck of genius lies in the winning ability he displays in persuading men, women, and groups that they simply cannot resist him unless they are out of their minds, blind, or utterly unfeeling. It works. He proves to be an easy touch if you praise him extravagantly enough, and he has been known to part with his last bucks for the girl who hasn't got quite enough in the bank to fly to Puerto Rico before the end of her third month. He might be the type to cut his right hand off for a friend if he happens to be in the right neighborhood, then to tirelessly remind everybody about it, forever. He embraced the credo of the swinger with all the energy of a crusading vegetarian, and is, in the art of love, half as good as he professes to be, which is pretty decent.

He finally walked up to us and asked me, his arms extended to Cass, whose youthful guts he hates, how I could deprive myself of his attentions for so long. I reminded him that I am a creature of accident, often prone to elude my own good. Ever since last year, Saul has kept calling me, trying to lure me back to him through gratitude, by sending me a few Johns, usually poor payers. From the tough professional league I now belong to there is no way back to the swinging circles, except on an occasional spree. My free time is scarce, and I will not waste my valuable id on a set of lunatics I keep in touch with just to play hooky and reassure myself that I am wanted and sought after, anywhere I care to reappear.

One night, this fall, I took Cass and Sheil to Saul's place for the first time. It was supposed to be a party of the kind he had accustomed me to, the previous year, a rousing hot session with couples fighting for lying space. It ended up being just old Saul in his auction-sale Roman chair, barefoot and kimono-clad. He ordered food from Chinatown Louie and Amylnitrite from a Seventh Avenue drugstore. Cass had to help him pay both bills. The evening was a bore, even with the two scrawny Lesbians who joined us later—Cass remarked that they looked like the kind of things I had been painting lately. They had brought a bunch of faded, drooping tulips. They used the innocent defenseless flowers to tickle each other's underarms and fannies. Some people hate flowers.

Before his show was over—he sold a single painting—Mika came back once to see me, bringing me black olives, Greek goat cheese, and wine, along with a check he hid under the rug, so thoroughly that it took me quite some time to retrieve it. He told me about his serene life in an old water mill in the Georgia hills, where he paints, and carves his frames himself. He asked me to come and visit him in the spring. He would teach me how to mix wax and glue. He would show me the blooming fields around his home. He would pay for my trip. He would prepare his best room for me. All he did was caress my nude body and kiss my breasts. I did not find his ruined flesh ridiculous. He was close to tears when he left me. He was moving his show to Washington. He had done very poorly in New York and lost money on the whole venture. Washington was giving him another chance. Washington owed him that much.

4

February 19th

Jim the Prophet was right when he foresaw certain troubles brought upon my head by a mercenary blonde's scorn: Lorrie calls me one morning to charge me with treachery, foul play, and double-dealing. She darkly predicts a cloudy future for one who does not "go by the book." I fail to convince her that I did not get loads of cash from Jim, a house on the Cape, and a perpetual annuity.

Cass informs me, the same week, of Lorrie's attempts to get Sheil to work for her. It seems that our fiery blonde is not doing too well with her own flocks. She is looking for sweet little beginners and sends Gene Davis after them. Gene heard about Sheil from gossipy Mister Clean. Sheil knows Lorrie is poison, but she says she can hold her own. She will be joining Lorrie's stable any time now. Cass is looking forward to meeting Lorrie to try and tame her "and so keep her from mistreating our Sheil too much." The honorable good Samaritan! He counts on me to brief him on how to whip Lorrie. He counts on Sheil to give him a thorough build-up as the most commendable bruiser in town. He counts on his countless charms to convince us both to pitch in for him.

I warn him: "You have no genuine feeling for it. You'll be a flop. She'll end up clobbering you. I wish you wouldn't get involved with that kink anyhow."

Why, oh, why couldn't I keep my mouth shut? But I add, without transition: "Well, all right, I'll let you have a couple of instruments."

I search for ways to put Lorrie on my side and ensure her neutrality. I soon have a scheme cooked up. Cass helps me, by keeping me up to date with the latest developments. He has used my paddle a few times on Lorrie. She does not call it a licking; she calls it "treatment." It makes her almost pleasant for a couple of hours. Sheil, however, is losing weight and sleep, harassed and weepy after two weeks of Lorrie's fits. Whenever a customer short-changes Sheil or keeps her too long, Lorrie blames her and calls her names. Sheil does not mind a few rash words now and then, but a steady diet of them proves trying for her nerves. This is the way Lorrie loses all her girls. Her bills are piling up high, her kickbacks remain too few. Her need for money needles her to peddle marijuana openly around town. It is suicide. She dreads sex so much that she handles tricks herself only as the last extreme, when she can send nobody else.

She is not the kind of enemy you can afford to neglect. Impatient to carry out my plan, I call her, bracing myself against the shock of her shrill voice.

"Lorrie, this is Lily."

I hear her catch her breath. I raise my voice: "Before you have time to spit at me, which would clog your phone unnecessarily, let me tell you first that I have a proposition for you, which could be carried out only if you were willing to forget about our past misunderstanding."

At last her answer comes through, diffidently: "I am listening."

"I thought about you for this job, because of the way you feel about me. It will be the perfect incentive for a good match. The man's name is Mark Haendel. You may know him."

"I don't."

"He is a literary agent. His *raison d'être* is girl-wrestling. He set me up three times last year against opponents of his choice. He asked me this week to furnish him with a challenger of *my* choice. The thing is done in his office, early evening. We first have to watch movies of professional girl-wrestling filmed in Germany and Japan. Be sure to express appreciation. Then he makes us strip to our undies and we set to work, with clenched teeth. It'll be easy for you to look fierce. No need to say we play it easy and he knows it, but it must not be too obvious. We must give him enough of a good show to make him get to town, right on the spot, so none of us has to play lovey-dovey with him after the floor show."

"Do you mean he relieves himself, just watching us?"

"With luck, yes. I got the impression that you hate my guts and that may make it difficult for me to lick you, but I sure will try."

She laughs, not too agreeably. I know she will rise to the challenge; but she has to fight it a bit: "What if I'm not interested?"

I am prepared for that one: "Then I will call a girl named Sandy. (I just made her up.) She is about my size and weight, too. I thought I'd give you first choice: Mark likes me to fight bitchy blondes."

"What's the fee?"

"A hundred for each. It's all set. Sandy is all ready to fill in for you and mess up her blond wig Friday night at five-thirty."

"Well, it's not enough money for that kind of insanity, but I have bills to pay. I'll take the job."

"We may have to do a bit of rehearsing. Also, Mark wants us to wear regular girdles, the kind that's open in between the legs. No panties. I'll wear black. You'll wear pink or blue. No white, remember, he's allergic to it. I'll have my hair combed up. Do whatever you want with yours. I'll come to get you at quarter to four, Friday. We'll have time to try a few holds and flips. Till then, don't daydream too much about damaging me. The rules are: no hair-pulling, no scratching, biting, or kicking."

"Don't be infantile. I'll be waiting for you Friday and you'd better show up. High heels of course?"

"High heels, and don't tell me I'd better show up! I am not going to foul things up for myself. Mark sends me a few of his friends for the regular bit, and I want to disappoint him just as little as I want to marry you."

I should not have told Cass about the sporting event. I have quite a job convincing him that I can't take him along as a referee. The poor lamb will have to be contented just screwing old Susan Friday night.

I call him Saturday morning. His sleepy growl snaps right back into eager clarity when he recognizes my voice. He must bear the torture of not elucidating his questions too much, because of Susan's ponytail on his pillow.

"Cass, Lorrie scratched me right under the left eye with her pinkie fingernail. But I am sure she did not absolutely mean it. We are that chummy now."

"Don't speak so loud, Bob, I can hear."

"Don't start Bobbing me. Susan owns you or something? That Lorrie . . . ! She won, she did. She is one inch and a half taller than me and three pounds heavier. I must say that the will to win was there. I didn't make it easy for her. You should have seen her bounce off that rug. I had planned to let her get me and I found myself fighting for my life instead. Boy, she sure needs a whipping now."

"What did they say at the office?"

"Oh, that crap again! She snobbed Mark so much that I thought he was going to throw her out. Finally he decided to take it as a joke. He had Scotch, bourbon, rye, vodka, gin, vermouth, rum, brandy, pernod and champagne on ice, and she wanted crème de menthe! She said nasty things about Yale men and I couldn't shut her up. Poor Mark was getting glazed eyes. She asked who decorated his office, and when he answered, sort of stiffly, she said, 'It *had* to be Don Ebstein, he hasn't been the same since Jacques left him.' But in the ring, glory be to God, she had to keep quiet except for sighs and groans, and she acted so hateful that Mark hit the ceiling twice. She called me 'honey' in the cab."

"So they were happy about the stock?"

"Sure, you know what they did with it?"

Susan's voice puts an end to my profanities.

I do one more thing for Lorrie. I introduce her to Russell Green. As a frustrated socialite, Lorrie, though she does not get much money out of him, goes for rides around the park in Russell's crop-swinging company. She tries hard to crack the close circle of his friends. I soon have poor Russell all fidgety about a number of intrigues and slanders, now shattering his once peaceful riding club. Russell attempted to be funny with me once. And Lorrie is learning to ride.

Jim Brent does not sound happy at my handling of Lorrie, and repeats dully over the phone that she is dangerous; but he is too aware of his responsibility in the situation to criticize my efforts to turn her into a friend.

She twice calls me over to help her entice and submit to her will two of the docile clients who come to her to be whipped. With the help of Jim, she had, earlier in the year, advertised in *Atone in Tune* her talent in dominating and punishing the opposite sex, and even though she has destroyed, in some fit of rage, most of the answers that came her way, she has honored a few of them with her attentions.

She handles her craft without intelligence, passing abruptly from uncalled-for social niceties to flippant despotism, giving her puzzled victim a Scotch sour with her right hand and directing him to her bed with the crop held in her left hand. My part, on those occasions, is to aggravate, by my mocking comments, the humbled customer, witness his whipping, then provide him with sexual comfort—if he can afford that bonus. Lorrie never caters to that herself, she knows that a slave must in no circumstance desecrate his mistress through common pollution. But except for that gross breach of the rules she avoids none of the other mistakes underlined in the aforementioned book of discipline, neglecting finesse in the whipping and interrogation of the victim, to name just one of her inadequacies.

She has learned nothing from Jim. It is all fairness for me to replace her in his affections. My master is soon to minister to me again. He announces his arrival a week ahead of time. He will stay at the Vanderbilt. I am then contemplating a move from Carpenter Street. I have my eye on a two-room apartment on Twenty-sixth Street, between Third and Lexington Avenues. The current tenant, an impoverished homo who used to blow a sad flute in a West-Side Greek club, is not paying his rent, and the landlady, intent on erasing Sodom's mark from her doorstep, threatens him with eviction. His platonic girlfriend, Gretchen Hamptudt, of ex-stripping notoriety, still uses the place as a hideout, for days in a row, opening the door to the liquor-store errand boy with not a stitch of black lace or a fox tuft on her faded, unemployed flesh. I must wait two more weeks before letting Babylon succeed to its sinning sister city. I feel sorry for the Hellenic folk lovers I may deprive of their dwelling, but, in this day and age, it is every flute for itself.

The rent is a hundred and nine, the ceilings are way up high and the southern exposure guarantees good light. That unassuming portion of Twenty-sixth Street shelters an important Polish foundation, a small printing shop, a lampshade factory, one Chinese laundry, one Puerto Rican grocery, and one boardinghouse for the deaf. Both avenues attract worshippers of art books and antiques, and the businessmen who lunch at Frankell's, Luchowitz, and the Dunked Mermaid.

This second weekend with Jim will be a turning point in our fantasies. We cannot let ourselves be carried away (which is a good enough occasion for curtailing probable excesses), thin walls and malignant echoes welcoming us at the Vanderbilt. I try the whip on my leg, while Jim tiptoes along the hall past our door, hearing all too clearly the telltale noises.

The necessity to be discreet makes us appeal to our Alma Mater, Imagination, and I owe Jim many stirring moments as the heroine of his evocations. We sit close together, not even touching, while I am taken to the slave market to be auctioned and sold after a public whipping meant as a tryout.

My eyes are closed, the room dark, Jim's voice at turns far away, sharp, soothing, pressing, to fit the happenings. I feel the cool chains pulling at my ankles, the prompt disrobing of my body, the sting of the brand, the buyers' hands on me, those of the dealer as he pushes me forward, down a few splintery wooden steps. . . . Figures are thrown into the bargain. I hear the boasting of the barkers. The price is going down a bit. I flinch under the probing fingers that find faults, count my teeth, and poke at the tightness of my faked virginity. My wrists fight against the rusty ring they have been tied to, up on the portal. I twist and sway, sobbing under the strap laid on my back to test and ensure my docility.

Before dinner, that first day, Jim takes me to Thirty-seventh Street, to Aunt Bess's umbrella shop. Using rain apparel as her front, this formidable elderly lady—she is a dignified six feet two—keeps, in the back room of her store, a few well-trained employees who stuff, braid, and cut leather and assemble the thin or thick, wide or narrow, straight or stiff strips and strands into paddles, straps, crops, and cats-o'-nine-tails that are not meant for the back of the New York horse. The assortment of canes, made of bamboo or pliant birch, would compete with any English school arsenal.

The clientele, an impeccably clean-cut crowd of all ages and both sexes, keeps in close touch with the latest articles. Regular buyers are personally informed through the mail of the workshop's most recent achievements. In the store, on the left side, behind a thick glass pane— beware of the discipline-minded kleptomaniac . . . O the thrill of being chastised with a stolen instrument—lies the striking collection of weapons, facing an equally bountiful array of umbrellas and canes.

The left-wing and right-wing devotees sometimes exchange good-natured sophisms, and an even number of dares and bets, none of which have been known to be carried through inside the store.

Jim must drag me through the door. I have vainly tried to bribe my way out of this ordeal by suggesting a number of abject penances I stand ready to submit to, if I am allowed to wait outside. But Jim, at his titillated best, asks for my advice in his most doting New England voice, as a respectful young salesman leans at attention over the counter.

"Dear, what do you think of that silver-handled cane? I daresay it looks quite flippant. Now the thongs on that cat might be a bit thick, but we know of circumstances when thongs could come in handy. What is the matter, darling? You look flushed. . . ."

The West-Pointish clerk expresses nothing on his well-scrubbed face but eagerness, and it takes him five elaborate minutes to wrap in orchid-pink tissue paper the fly chaser that Jim made me pick: this is Aunt Bess's last brainstorm, a cloud of silky filly mane dangling from a bamboo stick.

Jim makes me sleep that night with both wrists and ankles loosely cuffed and the new fly chaser hanging from the headboard above my face. Next morning, as a waiter rolls the breakfast up to our suite, taking what seems like years to lay the table and pour the coffee, I have to stay on my tiptoes up on the bathtub ledge, my arms tied to the shower's faucet, dressed even to my gloves and scarf but minus panties, with my skirts trussed up and pinned at the waist. Jim has left the bathroom door ajar, just enough to let me eat my heart out in fear that I might slip or stumble and cry out. I am being punished for working my wrists out of the cuffs, at dawn. But Jim will not carry out the threat of letting me go without breakfast; he is not that ruthless.

5

March 10th

"Allo?"

"Lily Duke? This is Ossie Shadduck. I'm the photographer Will Fraser tol'y'about. Looks to me Will wants some shots of you so I guess we'll have to get together some time to do it."

"Oh yes, Mr. Haddock. Will mentioned you last week."

"Not Hadduck! Shadduck! Sorry for pointin' it out. I'm sort of vain about my Indian blood. Well, what about tomorrow?"

The voice, deep and blurred, sounds as if this man quit school in the first grade.

"I may not be free tomorrow afternoon, and I'm not sure about the evening. Would you mind calling me again, same time, day after tomorrow?"

"Repeat that, will you? Man, it's too much. Will wasn't wrong about that accent. How long you been around? I mean in this free country an' all?"

"Long enough to know what good English sounds like."

"Not bad. What made you pick a goofy name like Lily?"

"It's the right name; it's the business that's goofy."

"Oh, so you're not so crazy about your schtick?"

"Schtick?"

"That's junkie talk. You'd beter get used to it. Your schtick, your racket, your line of work, unnerstand? Wow, it's gonna be tough talking to you, sir. You know how they call you? 'Frenchie.' It's a name for a pig, if you forgive me for sayin' so. You don't sound like a pig, but with Will's girls I don't expect nothin' else. Man, last time. . . ."

I manage to cut in: "This seems like quite a corporation."

"What did you think it was? My . . . we got a green one there. I bet you have no idea what kinda publicity the boys give you 'round here. You'd better wise up. You ain't been too smart up to now, from what Will say."

I glare at the receiver.

"Listen, Mr. Shadduck. It is true that I don't know what Will Fraser is up to and I don't like his ways, but I can tell even less about you and if you think you can get me all mixed up. . . ."

For some reason I am confused and my voice becomes so shaky that a shocked silence on the other side of the line replaces the wise retort I was expecting. So I go on, aware of some temporary weakness in my tormentor: "Anyhow, you said you were on Will's team or whatever you call it. Meaning he must use you too, any chance he gets. So don't tell me. . . ."

"Yeah, I play dumb with him. That's my strength. I screw him every time. That stud thinks he's got me, but he has it all fucked up. You can't screw a junkie. Never. You know what? I like you. Maybe you're not too bright and all, but I think I'll give you the inside on Will, so you don't let the cookie crumble the wrong way. I'll talk to you tomorrow."

He calls the following day at four-thirty. I am sewing buttons on a coat, a glass of Alka-Seltzer close at hand.

"Hi, so-called Lily. Gettin' all ready for the setup?"

"What do you mean?"

"Come on, Uncle Ossie knows everything. News travels fast. You got a big thing cookin' up, right? A fat juicy job from that greasy wop, Nick, who was with Will at the Stocking Tops yesterday. Didn't they call you from there?"

"Yes, but. . . ."

"You're supposed to do a convention tonight, for them, all by your sweet self. Some break. Like ten or twelve guys. But Nick wants to see what you can do first and he pays you a visit last night. I was downstairs in the car with Caddie, the fat schmuck you met last week. He said you weren't worth twenty-five, but he wanted to come up anyhow, right after Nick. I had to hold him pinned behind the wheel, I figured you'd have enough after Nick, the way he was plastered. I knew he wouldn't pay you nothin' too. . . ."

"What do you know about tonight?"

"You're waitin' for the big call now, right? Your hair is set, your dress has been pressed. Maybe they'll call soon. Maybe late. When they do, you just sit tight. It's a lulu of a snow job. They think they can talk in front of me. Once in a while I feel like cutting them good and I spill. If the girl is wise she'll figure it out for herself pretty soon, but you strike me as a real dumb one and I don' mind givin' you a break. So here's how they play the game. . . ."

"Who is playing games?"

"They are. Don't interrupt. They'll give you a guy's name. You're supposed to meet him an' all the others and Will and Nick an' all, in such and such a hotel, such a room number, and they set the time. You show up there and there's nobody, or some old lady who don't know you from the Pope. So you go back home and wait. By the time they call you, you're a nervous wreck. They give you hell like you never. . . . They say you must have knocked on the wrong door, or you were one and a half hours late: they told you seven-thirty, not nine, and you screwed everybody up and you'd better make it up to the gang, because the fellows are sort of disgusted with you, so next time a big job come along, you're *out*, unless you really go out of your way being nice to the whole bunch. What was that?"

"But why?"

"Everybody's got to have some fun, that's why. I don't say they'll drop you. Not yet. It ain't they're mad at you or somethin'. They want to see how far they can go. They're playin' the game. Will wants to show you who's boss. And I hate it when a bitch don't know the score and can't fight back."

"You're calling me. . . ."

"In my talk, it means just plain woman. Like a stud is a man. Take no offense. What's bugging you now?"

"I don't see why they should do this."

"Man, you're not cut out for the job. What's your name in real life?"

"You couldn't pronounce it."

"So I come over an' you write it for me. I can teach you lots more and you got lots to learn. You don't need to be afraid. Ex-junkies can turn their sex off like a faucet. Deal?"

I am wearing faded nylon pajamas, a big sweater, and cheap Japanese slippers. I sew one more button before the doorbell rings. I don't know what I expected but I am surprised.

Ossie Shadduck is about five feet nine, bearded, bow-legged, and sloppily dressed. He has black curly hair, like a Negro, bushy eyebrows over watery brown eyes, a heavily lined face, thin lips and a crooked nose. He wears a black chiffon scarf around his neck, soaked in Woolworth cologne, and he keeps sniffing at it without a word. He looks a badly lived-in thirty-five. A soft bulging stomach stretches his trousers' top. His restless eyes are not easy on me, but they light up at my record-player.

"The lady likes music."

He looks both peeved and bored. Takes his shoes off because it is raining outside, sits on the rug, lights a cigarette, grabs an ashtray, and starts talking before I have said three words.

"Now, what do you want from me, squaw? You dig soft soap or you'd rather take your medicine? I got a feelin' you scare easy, rabbit. No, I don't want no ginger ale, but if you had something like milk. Yes, M I L K. Excuse if I spell it. You may have noticed my speech is not the best there is and that's why. No, I don't need no glass. Give me that container if you can afford to waste it all on me. So all right, I was supposed to be with Will Fraser and Caddie—they also call him Rollsey—the night they had you in Kim's place last week, to size you up, so to speak. I had a late shooting and couldn't make it. Will had told me about you an' all. I was to take you to the studio after they was through welcomin' you, and, well, photograph you for Will's files. He had said: 'Man, you don't have to worry, it's there for you.' That simple. Hey . . . wait a minute. Don't look at me like that. Stay put. I'm just Ossie, and I ain't done nothin'. I got to tell you things as they are, or it's no good. You can stop me any time you like and show me the door."

I take a deep breath and pronounce: "Go on."

He unfolds his arms to gesture: "Will just can't figure all men ain't dogs like him and I don't dig the scene when a girl come across free—because she know she's expected to—if she wants to make a buck the next day. Will feels like doin' me a favor like a free piece once in a while when he's been owin' me bread too long and it ends up with me lecturin' the hell out of the broad for bein' such a dope. And Will thinks I had a ball. He pays me for the shooting when I yell too much—he got a thing about noise—but most of the time he thinks he pays me with the broad, and since I don't want no Will Fraser takin' me for a schmuck, I let him think what he likes. It ain't worth breakin' my ass explainin' to him how junkies trade their balls for the needle. 'You don't even have to put no film in the camera, Ossie boy,' he says. 'Once you got her stripped, after a few cute sittings, you're in business, man.' He knows I don't go for the no-film-in-the-camera bit, but he says it anyhow. I think a girl is entitled to have a few prints of her tits or something if it makes her feel good. In that studio—I mean pig-pen—there's always some lousy film on the floor. So it makes her happy, and it don't bug me. It's not Will's business, it's mine. He don't own the studio. Not that I do, yet, but maybe some day, if I keep clean, I'll be a partner. If

I use my noodle. It was me had the idea about Will gettin' all the broads in glossy black-'n-white with measurements typed in back and sendin' the photographs ahead, all over the country, to the companies that hold conventions in New York. I done the thinkin', I done the shootin'. Will's been takin' all the credit. He's lousin' it up too: takin' too many chances with mailin' and things."

I cut in: "Well, he is not going to mail *me*."

He levers himself upright, making a face: "To go back to the girls, most of the time I let them talk to me while I shoot. You chicks sure love to talk. I guess I look like Jesus Christ. Was the same damn thing in the clink. Most o' the time, I don't take the trouble of wisin' em up to Will. They're too dumb. I just bawl 'em out. But you look like you could use your brains if you tried. So I figure I'm not wastin' my breath, am I? Man, you look sick. I got more bad news: I know things about you I shouldn't. You have no idea how those studs talk. Not just Will, Leo too. Take that Americana convention. I know the dame who was supposed to pull it; they dropped her because, right now, you're news. I heard you done somethin' extra that night and didn't charge no extra fee for it. Man, you must be crazy. Not so many broads take it up there. If word gets around you sell yourself that cheap, you're finished."

I have not stopped sewing. It seemed safer from the start to keep my hands busy while I was being lectured. Now, my needle stopped in midair, I force myself to look at this man.

He is making sense and stripping me to the bone. I have turned crimson. I hate myself for it. Ossie is holding a mirror to me, I have my back to it. I feel naked and spread apart in front of him, all on hearsay.

"One more thing, since you're close to bawling already. They say you run around with nothing on. I don't say it don't look good; but it sure looks cheap. Lots of pigs do it? That's just why you shouldn't. Wear a nightie or something. Not flimsy. Make those studs think it's a god-dam privilege to see you stripped. Drop that nightie at the last minute. It's not what you show that count. It's what you hide. You ever been to the movies? You're no raving beauty, but you got some class. You got to play that up. If you got to be a prost, be the best you know how. And don't wear no sexy bikinis. Wear them plain cotton panties. Not sheer stuff. Be different. You're just the kind of girl that should be. Boy, you sure can cry. I hate it, damn it. Listen, don't mind me. I'm nothin'. I just know the bit, that's all. You don't have to tell me it stinks. I got a nose too. You don't have to feel bad in front of me or anything. I'm the best guy to wise you up because I don't matter. You want me to scram? Hey, listen, stop. Oh all right, go on. Just turn around, if you don't mind. I hate women crying. They look so dopey. And I always think it's my fault, that maybe I'm clumsy or somethin'."

Suddenly I am mad: "I can cry if I want to; I am in my own home. I am not upset. I cry because it makes me feel good. I haven't done it for two weeks. I need it. And, by the way, you *are* clumsy."

He yells too. "All right, fine, cry. I'm sorry I can't think of nothin' terrible to tell you no more. I said it all. Man, you are messy. Here's an ashtray. Your nose is swellin' somethin' awful. If Nick an' Will could see you like that, they'd kick you out in no time. Hey, you haven't written your name for me yet."

64

"It's Aimée. You are going to make it sound like Emmy. Everybody does."

"Even Emmy sounds better than Lily. Listen, I got to cheer you up. I'll tell you about myself so you see you don't have to feel no shame. Everything is rosy close to junk. You're like sweet Virgin Mary lookin' down at old Judah. Number One, I was a whore myself, sort of part-time. I peddled my you-know-what when I was a sailor. I used to look cute and lean, ten years ago, and fags liked the back of my neck. Blow your nose. I was a thief. A terrific one. I had genius. I done so much time in jail, all over the States, that they made plans to name one after me. I was an artist with the torch. . . . If you ever need anybody to bust a drugstore, the name is Shadduck: S H A . . . all right. Once, when I needed a fix too bad to stay home babysittin', I left my kids alone. My wife had to go out and work nights; all the money I stole was for junk. My youngest kid fell from his cot and went crawlin' to the kitchen. He got hold of the matches and how they didn't both burn to death I'll never know except my wife came back early 'cause she felt sick. She opened the door when the curtain started to go up in flames. It sounds like a B picture, but it's the truth. I been close to killin' a few people a few times. If I didn't, it was because some other stud done it. You know, fights between junkies. For junk. Nothin' else worth fightin' for. And when I hit somebody, I finish the job unless you stop me. There was always somebody to stop me. I had good friends then. Now, would you please show me if you look half decent when you smile, and since it don't look like you're gettin' no call from them jokers, what about playin' some of those records?"

65

I am groggy. I decide to eat. He does not want anything and watches me work on a box of chocolate-chip cookies. He reads all the record jackets. I see him select Chopin, Handel, Beethoven, Vivaldi, and Stravinsky. He puts them on very low and whistles along softly in counterpoint, chain-smoking. It is getting late. The phone rings a few times but nobody answers my hello. Ossie's jeering voice again: "That's them. They'll tell you tomorrow your phone don't work. By the way, I'm not keepin' you from nothin'? Just say so."

I answer: "I have nothing planned. I was keeping the evening for Nick and Will. It is too early to go to sleep, I suppose, but I'll just lie on my bed, if you don't mind. I have cramps, I'm tired."

"The music don't bother you? I'll turn it lower if you like."

"Keep it just like that."

I take my sweater off, jump out of my slippers and lie on top of the bedspread. I do not fear this man. The rain beats at the window. The refrigerator hums and stops and starts again. I hear it between Handel and Albenitz. The janitor, next door, is hammering on some pipes.

Ossie asks: "May I light a candle? I'd like to read that stuff on Beethoven. Candles get me where I live. Around the eyeballs—I can't stand bright lights."

The last thing I am aware of, before falling asleep, is Ossie's voice reading something aloud about violins. When I wake up, he is still reading, and it is close to midnight. Crouched low on a small chair, he lifts his head up. "Go back to sleep, will you? And open up your bed, it'll help."

I do what he says.

At eight o'clock next morning, I sit up on my bed and I look straight into a pair of red-rimmed eyes that stare at me from the same corner of my room, from the same low chair. The air is thick with cigarette smoke. The sun shines through the drapes. He asks: "That what you call sleeping?"

"Hm?"

"You yelled in French. You babbled in English. You tossed around. You sat up and growled. You snored. You got hold of a corner of the headboard and kissed it. You put your legs up in the air and kicked around. You knocked yourself on the head a couple of times. You almost fell out of the damn bed twice. You tried to reach for the rug, down there. You played ball with the pillow. It was such a show an' all that I decided to stay. How can you ever talk a man into sleepin' with you twice? I guess you don't like your schtick, all right. Not deep down. I'm sorry I was so rough on you yesterday. I can't even say I didn't mean it, cause I did."

He is standing now, and picking up his Eisenhower jacket. So he was not glued to that chair after all. He is going to leave. I motion him to come closer. He does, awkwardly. I pull his head down to me and kiss his scratchy cheek.

After he has left, I make coffee. He said he did not want anything.

April 2nd

Ossie snaps his fingers at the cabbie: "Man, I left my baby at the studio. Dad, wait for me just a sec. . . ." and, to me, "I'll be right back, sweet."

He gets out of the cab in front of a Times Square novelty shop, disappears, stooping, through the garish entrance, comes back with a knife which he drops in his shirt pocket—a brand-new baby—fishes nine bucks, all creased singles, out of same pocket, pushes the bills down his left sock and we are ready for Harlem. He says that Harlem is always ready for him.

"I'm gonna show you my people tonight, sweet. I'm welcome up there any time of the day or night. You wait and see. I won't give you no build-up. Just be ready for the worst and if you see a rat, don't shriek."

I have been cooped up in my bedroom all day, my hands full with an accountant from Queens, an architect from Connecticut, a dental student, and a Bronx laundry-chain owner. One hundred and forty-five dollars.

When Ossie came up at seven-thirty, I had a soaked towel on my forehead and a soothing ointment on my groundfloor. I felt beat. I wanted to stay home and read in a hot bath, but Ossie insisted about the right sort of rain outside and argued me into a tweed skirt, fuzzy sweater, and flat-heeled shoes.

"Just a drizzle, sweet, it'll put you together in no time."

The cab zooms uptown. We get out in a rancid-smelling street. The rain has stopped. Steam surrounds us. The glow of cigarettes outlines the doorways and fire escapes. A match flickers, thrown from a top floor. Ossie bends over the rail next to a flight of steps. He whistles twice, softly. He is holding my arm firmly and I have to lean with him. No answer. We go around the corner and stop in front of an open bar on the avenue.

A shadow jumps at us before we are through the bar door. Ossie introduces Beans, who pumps my hand limply with an absent: "I'm sure pleased." Beans is light on his feet, small and flashy. One of his front teeth is missing. He wears a green cap with the flap turned to the back of his head. His face twitches under the neon signs. He nibbles at a toothpick. The two men hug each other tenderly, like French country girls.

"We been whistling for you down there, baby," Ossie says, squinting at Beans, his feet wide apart.

"I had to see the Turk's brother, but it's no dice." The slight Negro seems to shrink under the light.

"How is Rebecca?"

Beans straightens up.

"So so, takin' it easy. Her partner been put away, and you know my Becky don't work alone."

Ossie punches his friend in the ribs, not so playfully.

"I know you wouldn't let her, man. Everything she knows, she learnt it from you. And you ain't dumb yet."

Beans smiles, his thick, purple tongue showing. He dodges a second punch. Rebecca is his woman. She used to hook. "But," Ossie says, "Beans won't stand for it no more." She picks pockets in the subways and department stores to supply both her man and herself with enough "horse" for them to stay happy. Beans is too hot right now to go back to his schtick. He used to be Ossie's partner. Since Ossie kicked the habit, Beans has been out of luck.

We go down through a strong urine stench to Beans's cellar. Leaking pipes keep the dirt spongy under our feet. Cats prowl around, grown huge on the abundant supply of rats. Cots are piled high with torn blankets, oily rags, and snoring occupants. Broken glass crunches and jingles as we pass. Ossie lifts me in his arms across a pile of garbage. The back of the cellar closes in, shaping a private three-walled shelter that reveals a torn mattress, a ripped armchair, a kitchen table, a broken mirror scribbled over with lipstick, a closet.

"Wow, Beans, you fixed it real nice."

I look at Ossie. He is not joking.

"That's Becky's doing."

Beans is fairly bursting with pride. Ossie explains:

"See, sweet, I lived here with Beans for years, but at the time the place was sort of run down."

I notice a bug-killer spray can on the closet. That's class.

Ossie gives Beans some pills that are supposed to help him hang on better, next time he is sick. I wonder if it is dexedrine. He also takes his money out of his sock and I look away, facing a bunch of spiders' webs on the back wall, thick as a robin's nest. I hear Beans make his exit and Ossie search the room. When I turn around, Beans is back, breathing noisily. From inside the armchair, they have extricated a small parcel, wrapped in brown paper, Beans's "works": the junkie's equipment. Beans now extends his arm to Ossie, who ties a dirty handkerchief around Beans's swollen wrist. Then Beans probes and misses for a long time, his fingers shaking, the sweat pouring from his brow, before his needle can select a good spot. His veins show very little and the swelling does not help.

"Look at that nigger's blood, sweet. Red like mine, ain't it? Not that I can pass for white no more, hey Beans? Beans?"

Beans's face is mollifying. He nods dreamily. He secures the same handkerchief around Ossie's wrist and shoots a "share of the bag" into his veins. I turn my back on them, trembling, keeping my mind a careful blank, drowning deep in their lazy talk. Their voices have become high-pitched, childlike.

"Old Cindy done it again, Os. Turned her own sons in,

last week. After everybody havin' a lean time and *she* was never sick. The cops give her a fat fix every day an' she supply 'em with names an' all. She gonna get knifed soon, I hope, an' she know it. She don't care. If she's high enough, she won't even feel no knife."

They laugh delightedly. Ossie lights a cigarette.

"I hear Timmy was found cold last night on the Polacks' roof. Greedy, he was. Be careful, Honey Beans, you're mighty careless yourself at times, and I'm not around no more to drag you to your feet and keep you hoppin' and hit you in the head. You got no sense when you're on your own. Man, I wish Becky was back."

Beans looks down at his crotch.

"*You* wish she was back, you mother! I ain't touched at nothin' since she gone."

Ossie explains, for my benefit and with more than a touch of pride, that Beans is the only junkie he knows who keeps his hunger for women. He makes it sound like such a rare distinction that I wonder whether I should congratulate Beans. But I find nothing to say and Ossie looks hurt.

At twelve-thirty, our host walks us to the corner. It is late, I am white, and a lot of people are starting to forget Ossie's face.

As soon as we are in the cab, I explode in Ossie's ear. "You dirty liar, you! Is that what you call being clean?"

"Wait a minute, sweet. I know how you feel. I was hopin' he wouldn't do it. You don't know what it's like. You don't know how a stud feels when his pal does him a favor and he can't give nothin' in return. The least a man can do is a little sharin'."

"And you are willing to take a chance like that!"

"Listen to me, will you! A skinny pinch like that couldn't put me back on the stuff in a million years. Beans knows that. Beans is proud of me for kicking. The last thing he wants is to see me back on the stuff. But when I give him bread to buy it, I have to let him give me a taste. A man gotta have manners. I can't hurt his feelin's. I kept hopin' he wouldn't do it, on account of you was there. That's why I didn't tell you nothin' in advance."

"And how often do you have those friendly little sessions?"

"It was the first time. Honest, since I quit. . . . I send him the money usually. But this time I had to see him myself on account Max is in the hospital. See, Beans is hot, right now. They're lookin' for him in the worst way. He been without it for two days, you seen how he was shakin'. When Becky don' work, I know he's sick and I send him a few bucks. Don't think he comes after me askin' for money. I'm the one who checks on him when I know Becky's not around. I call the bar on the corner, and the bartender go gets him. Bartender is Max, Becky's brother. Beans don't have to tell me nothin' about how he feels, how long he been without it, and so on. All I need is to hear his voice on the phone. I send him the dough through Max. Max is not on the stuff, and he wouldn't steal nothin' from me 'cause I got a coupla pretty things on him. But he been took sick this week, and Beans don't trust nobody else. Beans didn't mind you standin' there havin' a fit, 'cause he don' know how things are between us. He thinks you are my woman, and you don't question what I do."

6

April 10th

The Governor Clinton is the hotel where my husband, my baby, and I stayed for a week, eight years ago, freshly disembarked from the "Liberté" and hesitant about how to find an apartment in Manhattan. Was there really a time when I did not know about *The New York Times?*

Our room was on the twenty-second floor. From the window, I felt like a provincial Mrs. Gulliver, ready to seize the small colorful cars with a pair of eyebrow tweezers. I had it all upside down; there was indeed some upstairs Governor Gulliver grabbing his own Twinity-Tweezers to nab me and send me all the way down, where they say He located Hell.

Thirty-fourth Street awed me then. Today it is just one of the marketplaces where the garment kings, my customers, make their bread. American cars dazzled me then. Now I have been taken for too many off-color rides and my cheek hardly blushes, fluently conversant as it is with all the sorts of flannels, tweeds, leathers, corduroys, suedes, and seersuckers that can clothe a male car-driver, not to mention the different brands of zippers. But I still cannot tell a Pontiac from a Chevy, which shows you never learn.

Today I am not struck by lightning at the sight of the flashy evening shoes in Miles's windows. I have worn those lowlife rhinestone pumps during my Roseland nights, and the sluttish Cinderella magic has gone the way plastic heel tips go.

Today, as a friend of Karen, Lorrie's deserting lieutenant, I am calling the Governor Clinton Hotel and expressing my wish to speak to Jeff Finley, a very tiny washer or bolt in the big staff machine of that second-rate large palazzo. Jeff Finley is a small-fee-to-be on Karen's list, but after cashing in on the big spenders I have to wait till they contact me again, and I get busy on the petty fry.

Mr. Finley, in a nasal, over-fifty clipped voice, takes his time remembering about Karen, then sets our date for the next morning. Either Karen is not as good as she says she is, or this guy is at the age when even memories slip by.

I show up at ten o'clock the next day, straight from the beauty parlor, and ask for Jeff Finley. A pudgy, short-legged man introduces himself as Morton, Jeff's brother-in-law, and uses the inside phone to notify Jeff of my arrival, while trying to evaluate my measurements. I keep my cashmere coat loose around my bust and hips to give him a bad time guessing.

"Your guest is here, Jeff, old dog. Could I help you show her around? O.K. I send her up."

Twenty minutes later, his flat feet wide apart, goose pimples running on his white, swordfish flesh, his false

74

teeth clicketing, Jeff Finley is putting his shorts back on and looking for a cigar, in a narrow, damp room on the fourth floor that must be used steadily by the help for those specific ends.

"I have no money for you, tootsie. Business is bad. I'll give you a nice little watch from the shop downstairs. Don't tell me you can't use a watch . . . I see you're not wearing one."

He speaks in a quiet, final way, not a bit apologetic. It is my fault. After one look at that senile monkey, at that room, I should have asked to be paid first, but I am not used to that kind of clientele and I do not want to get used to it.

I will take his crappy watch, I will not throw it in his face. I look under the bed for my left shoe, pick up all my bobby pins and point at the lint-thick rug, the dusty formica: "Lousy service."

I go down the back stairs, ahead of him. I choose a watch in the gift shop's display glass counter and drop it in my handbag, wrapped in tissue paper. I turn my back on Jeff, who hurries away, much relieved, after knocking on the shop's office door. Morton rushes toward me. He wants to take me in that closet of a room, with standing place only. He would recline against the metallic files, I would kneel down, my face brushing his trousers. I know the song, lowest key and all. The gruesome discomfort of the scene would add to his kicks. There is a typewriter on a littered desk, cardboard boxes in a pile, a girlie calendar on the wall.

"I'll give you a twenty right away. Before I touch you. And maybe a coupla bucks for your cabfare. Here's the twenty: feel it in my pocket."

He makes me feel something else too. I pull my hand away without anger. I look at him curiously. He spits air bubbles when he speaks. I watch them clutter and explode at the corners of his lips. Everybody could see his hard-on if I were not blocking the view.

A few people go by and stop idly to look at the costume jewelry, evening bags, lighters, and ashtrays. Maybe Morty is missing a sale right now. Morty does not care. Morty is a small man with a small job, taking big, foolish chances. Nothing matters to Morty except getting me in that room, watching me open that coat, shrug out of my skirt, peel my stockings off. He might spit on me tomorrow (using all that available saliva), but today he wants me, even at the cost of his job. What is this longing of man for a woman's flesh, which for a few minutes of stolen, suspended time stills all other cares, silences all other voices within him?

Morty's loud whisper could be easily overheard, with half a try. He grabs both my sleeves urgently, and I hold onto my coat lapels for dear life. A doorman, a bellboy hang around, grinning, nudging each other.

I am not listening to the little man. I feel weak. I keep my body tilted back, away from him. Soon my strength will be returned and that worm shaken off my coat.

Right now I am shooting a movie, just for myself. A flashback that was news eight years ago. Today my naïveté is a bit rusty and I cannot gape at the reception desk's red velvet trimmings as does this girl on the screen.

Suitcases and bags are brought in. Some have European labels. A Cunard Line poster screams at me. I stare at it above Morton's shoulder and this drives him insane.

"Say, what's the matter with you, anyhow? You sick?

Listen to me. I won't treat you like Jeff did. He's an ass. You can see I'm not the same kind of guy. Honey, I go for your legs! Christ, I want to bang you! I want to kiss your thighs and the hair in between . . . I bet you got it all curled up and soft and pretty. I hope you're one of those French girls who don't shave their underarms, hey, honey?"

I will give Karen a few bucks out of my pocket, her share of the fee I was supposed to get from Jeff Finley. Morton's office is too close to the lobby, where more and more Air France luggage is piling. You must be crafty with your memories. You must bargain with them, then maybe they will leave you alone.

I walk to the exit. Morty is still pleading.

April 15th

The Casavecchias' beauty parlor is owned and operated by two of Frankie's brothers, Rocco and Dino. I used to swing with Frankie, in the days when I did not yet need to put any dollar-green ointment on my pussy.

I have found a way to have my nails and hair done for free—I mean, taken out in trade—before my evening East-Side jobs.

The shop is on Second Avenue in the Fifties. I walk in, around five-thirty, am shampooed by a not too neat Spanish girl who is wise to the whole thing and pulls at my hair a bit too much, although I tip her fifty cents. When and if she stops pulling, I will stop petting her boss: reading between hairlines that the three of us are perhaps sharing a couple of "pediculous pubis"—that's Latin for crabs.

Rocco sets my hair in haste, pinches my ear lobes now and then, and pushes his crotch hard against my elbow or my upper arm every time he manages to turn his back on the other customers and to keep the reflection of that semiprivate friction spot out of the indiscreet all-around mirrors.

From under the hair-dryers, I see the last customer, the shampoo girl, and Dino leave one by one, the last casting a hopeful glance toward me, which I ignore. I will not turn an appetizer into a full meal or a convenient fancy into a Rocco and Co. enterprise. Besides, Dino is on his way to having a Neapolitan potbelly.

Hidden by a plastic curtain, our lust nest looks like a fitting room, hardly bigger than a country vicar's wardrobe. This is where ladies exchange their coats and dresses for cotton smocks; a dozen clothes hangers dangle from the rail. A tall hassock faces the full-length mirror.

I rush under the curtain with Rocco, all my rollers still on, secured with a pink net. We have discovered that, in ten minutes of sex, I perspire so abundantly that Rocco has to put me back under the cool dryer for a while, right after the fun is over and before he hurriedly styles my hair.

"Make it snappy, Rocco. It could take me ages to find a cab."

He once drove me himself to Rear-Lover Herman's house, after detaining me a few minutes longer than usual.

I stand in front of the mirror, Rocco behind me. He unties my smock and lets it drop to the floor. He pulls my panties down and lets them rest around my knees. He

78

never lowers them farther. Here I am in bra, stockings, and garter belt. I enjoy to the full that state of semi-nudity, and my nether lips start to moisten up and part softly. In the mirror, Rocco watches his own spreading, stretching, invading fingers and my flaming, raving face. I watch him watch me. He could make me come this way if he prolonged that caress, but, being a greasy, cocky, Godfearing, dirty little guinea teaser, he does not admit I *deserve* to come and he stops me in midair, which makes me feel chastised and contented in a funny shamed way.

The hassock is just high enough to lift my stomach at the right level when he turns me over, still half peeking over his shoulder at the sight of my reflected exposed hindquarters he is so fully and rigidly disposed to take care of.

He tears his fly open as if it were stuffed with live coals and shows me the shrimp-pink, shining, bulging head of his crude, healthy ding-dong, slaps my face gently with it, swinging his hips, then, stepping to the back of the stool—and the back of me—for a short but vigorous while, he pushes his tool in and out of me, so savagely, so meatily, that my curlers nearly pop out.

My response never matches his questioning, but the narcissistic preliminaries enchant me. All along, I like to feel intimately observed and judged by that other couple of copycats in the mirror.

Rocco is expensive. When I want to combine him with an eight o'clock job, I have to keep free from five on, and it has happened that I turn down an early evening offer in order not to miss my mirrored thrills, not justified any more by a hair-to-be-set pretext, since I know very well that I should have my hair done in the morning, at some neighborhood beauty parlor, operated strictly by fags, which would cost me seven dollars and save me at least thirty.

April 19th

This Easter Sunday tastes breezy and bright, but, like an unsalted potato chip, it misses a definite measure of drama. There must be a mistake in the calendar. If not, I will have no regrets about using my time in the pagan fashion planned yesterday.

I shall have Sheil's company. She pulls me away from myself in a most welcome analgesic way. It is Easter, a day to suffer, unless you are reborn. But I already suffered yesterday, and the day before. So I have a right to skip this one, if I may.

Another Casavecchia, Gibb, short for Gianbattista, the youngest of the male brood, just married, has become one of my steady customers, which proves that anything can happen to a bad girl if she just keeps hoping and praying against odds and barking up the same old family tree.

Gibb, pretty lucky with the horses, a winner too with women, proves a huge shade more lucrative than his brother Rocco. He is starting a girlie magazine and he needs a few sets of black-stockinged legs. He is duly impressed by my own, but a bit vague about my bust, so I have talked Sheil into helping me out. She agreed there is not much we can do on Easter Sunday except plan more sinning, and Gibb Casavecchia's photographer is expecting us today for a twosome setting: thirty-five dollars' worth of saucy wrestling and mutual spanking.

Thirty-five dollars is a hell of a Sunday price, but our employer knows we will take it, because it will be the only offer of the day.

Phil Petersen stoops in front of me, in paint-spotted khaki shorts and torn leather booties. No shirt. No socks. He holds a soon-to-be-punctured beer can. His jaw-length hair falls straight and oily. His tattoos relegate any I have seen in that department to kindergarten level. His face is inhabited by a majestic settlement of skin worms. Streaks of black ink run an Aztec pattern on his left calf.

He moves a camera and a few magazines so that I can sit down facing him. His room comes up to the expectations you cannot help shelter at the mere mention of its address on an uptown side street between Columbus and Amsterdam avenues. Transient, as the seasons are.

It looks slept in, hidden in, worked in, and indiscriminately borrowed by and lent to a number of urgency cases of different degrees of acuteness and solvability.

The film reels that roll and unroll inside those four walls are certainly not of the most lawful variety. But that magazine work is going to be legitimate all the way down to black unsheer lingerie. No nude shots. Discipline in frills. Fighting, scratching, and biting in rags and tatters. Phil provides the rags.

Sheil is late. After showing off my undies, upon request and from a distance, I decline an offer of a drink and listen to Phil Petersen's sober vision of life. He is a seaman eight months of every year. He glumly states that it takes him all of those eight months to forget the taste of the four others. From his obvious, sustained exile from soap and water and barber's scissors, it looks and smells as if this man is telling the truth.

81

He starts debating about Cuba while I go through the pages of previous issues of the magazine Gibb is black-mailing away from its owners and remodeling after his own pan-Italian bookie taste. He will turn it into a super-duper private subscription cookie, unavailable to the Times Square common crowd, and handy to advertise, in foggy terms, the numerous stag movies the Casavecchia family has been financing and peddling for the last twenty years.

It proved to be a brutal afternoon. The more sailor Petersen sipped beer and indulged in socialistic digressions, the less speed he applied to his work. Putting the camera together took him about an hour of strenuous leisure. Sheil and I talked shop under our breath, referring to "typing assignments," "free-lance soloing," or "team work," under the benign knowing look of our host.

We must have provided Petersen's target with a hundred different angles on the fighting, clothes-tearing, bottom-paddling kink. There was no clock or watch around, so when Sheil finally hopped to the phone, Petersen stopped her: "It don't work, duckie." He went down and brought up coffee and donuts, fully satisfied that he had made our day in a grand manner.

A hibernating mood crept over me. I had nothing planned for the night. Same thing for Sheil. Cass was busy with "Somebody New's Roommate." Ossie was in the Bronx, doing a paint job in his mother's shop. After months of trying to break away from the swinging crowd, I had to admit I had succeeded. Through the dirty windowpane, the sun was drooping like a poached egg.

I knew I would go dancing that night, back to my

sources, if I had a chance, if I came home early enough to put my hair up. I did not want to wake up in Roseland with a bang and a Cuban waiter wrapped around my crotch. The fascination and anguish of it gave me chills.

Petersen asked us to "peel off the frills, sort of lie down and make with the snatch-eating bit, like two good sports," for ten dollars more. Draped in the remains of our rags, sweaty undies, as well as our dignity, we declined the magnanimous offer: we would not contribute to Philip Petersen's private files. He took it coolly, but did not try to change our minds. We left him alone to count his empty beer cans.

We had some coffee on Broadway. We were clinging together, that Sunday, with the same dread of going home to our separate rooms. Sheil described to me the new outfits she was getting at her dressmaker's. Born and raised in "Cabbage Town"—Toronto's wrong side of the tracks—amidst the heavily imbibing Irish, little Sheil today dishes out of the not-so-easy bucks she makes, in addition to the necessities she did not have as a little girl, the luxuries she yearned for then. It will take her a while to realize that the primrose path reeks of cabbage too.

We decided not to sign the release for those photographs. So we did not get our checks from Gibb's office. We had been careful to make faces at the camera or turn away from it right before the flash, but we started feeling funny at the idea of being pasted all over a number of glossy pages, private subscription or not. Only an exorbitant fee would have kept us from demurring at the deal. But Gibb let us know that "the damage could not be boosted." We were not disappointed. All we had wanted that day was to warm up our shoulders under the same Easter coat.

April 22nd

Talk, that's all they can do. That's what they come here for in the first place. The tough ones insist on answers and advice:

"I want your honest opinion, Lily. Now what is a *nice* girl likely to do when her boss. . . ."

"Here is what my partner says to me every time that I. . . ."

"Listen to my mother-in-law's latest brain storm. . . ."

"My teen-age daughter went into a fit because. . . ."

The easy ones are contented by basic encouraging noises such as: "Sure. . . . But of course. . . . Really? You mean that? Imagine!" or: "I'll be. . . ." The petty torments of middle age, the stitches of shattered ambition are dumped in my weary lap. I am made to listen to the crystallization of many an ulcer. Wives' anatomy of frigidity, knack for nagging or aversion to golf, martinis, off-color jokes, and card games, are served to me rare or sizzling, as I prepare myself for the closing last-minute ludicrous absolution: "But deep down she's a wonderful gal."

Now take this one. He has me by his paunchy side, at 11:30 P.M.; I am meeting him for the first time. The setting is one of those P. J. Moriarty funeral parlors. The action is pending and, for the moment, generously diluted in booze.

"Nice girl, Sheil, that's what she is. You got a good friend there. One of the best. Heart of gold. Smart kid, too. A lot of fun. Yes sir, that's a nice girl for you. Don't you agree she's one of the nicest girls around? You can depend on somebody like that. You're lucky you have her as a friend. The best you got, I bet. And she got brains too. She is nice people. Sheil really is.

"You drinking gin, eh? Cannot stand the stuff. I'm a Scotch man, yes sir. Always liked my Scotch. But you don't care for Scotch, right? Never touch it? Well, I'm one for Scotch. As for gin I don't even remember what it tastes like. But I like Scotch. Gee, I can't stay away from it. I'm not a drinking man, mind you. I just like to have a few once in a while. But I stick to Scotch. It's good for a man. What you drinking? Oh . . . well I never touch it. Like I said. . . .

"Hey Tim, how's the kid doing? Whaddya mean 'he's young?' He's twenty-two, that's how young he is. He cannot be an old son of a bitch like you, give him time, will you! Gee, it burns me up when I see people forget what it feels like to be young. Great, that's what. See, Lily, that's the kid, at the end of the bar. Pete, his name is. Just arrived from Dublin. He's a regular pain, but I sort of like him. He rubs me the right way. He don't like it too much here, he says, but the money is good. How do you like that! A regular pain. Whaddya mean he's young! This place can use a young bartender. All I see around is old jokers like me. Depressing. Let me tell you, honey, when I was twenty, I was the biggest jerk who ever lived.

I didn't know any better, see. But I had fun. That's because I didn't know any better. Where did it all go? Now I'm so wise that I con myself half the time. So he says he don't like it here so much, but the money is good! Well, why don't he go back to Dublin? He's too young for this place anyhow. He's a prize jerk.

"Another one for me, Tim. The little lady doesn't touch hers. No wonder: it's gin. Look at the dainty way she smokes. She used to be a teacher, see?

"So how's Sheil? That's a nice kid for you. The last time I called her she said she was having dinner in front of TV all by herself. I ask you: wasn't that too much: all by herself with a steak and the old TV! I says: 'Sheil, for Pete's sake, you could call me when you're alone! Don't you go and have dinner all by yourself! I'll take you to a restaurant, just any time.' She says: 'I don't want to bother you, Ken.' That's the kind of girl she is. She has *feelings*. I swear to God this girl has. 'I don't want to bother you.' She has that cute lisp. Not much. Just a touch. And she gets lonesome, I know, eating dinner all by herself and sitting with her steak, her wig, and her luscious big tits in front of the lousy commercials. But she says: 'I don't want to bother you, Ken.' Because she has *manners*. They don't make girls like that any more.

"What was I saying? Oh yes, tits. No, I said something before, about Florida, didn't I? I can't take that New York winter anymore. A winter that lasts four whole months. I got arthritis. I'm lucky I'm in show business: I can do just as good in Florida. Take care of everything from there. New York is not what it used to be. My doctor says to me: 'Best thing is to settle down in Miami Beach, and fly back to New York in the summer.' Because of arthritis and everything. A little golf, a little sunbathing, a little fooling around. This town here used to be something special. Now I have a bellyfull of it. A bellyfull of hot air. So my doctor says: 'Pack up and go South.' On account of arthritis and everything.

"Say, you're not afraid of dogs, are you? I got my Pepper at home. He's a big Dobermann. Two years old and not a mean bone in his body, 'cause I trained him right. He's a champ. A stud. Worth over a thousand clams now. I call him Pepper. I got him when he was a pup. I give him all his shots and the best food there is and take him out and horse around with him in the park, and see to it that he has a little lady between his hind legs once in a while. He's not like us fumbling people. Every time he goes he scores. Bang. Take you and me, baby, we are going to make it, I hope, but chances are you'll still have your little flat stomach six months from now, at least there's a good chance you will. But my Pepper he never misses. Don't be scared of him. He'll jump at you and crawl all over you 'cause he's playful, but he's good-natured as long as you let him have his way. You should see his fangs. His daddy was trained to kill during the war. And can he growl when he is mad! I had him as a pup. Even then he had a temper.

"You're a quiet girl. Quite a girl, too. Ha ha. Sheil told me you had a small bust. Well you can't have everything, right? Take me: I got good shoulders still, and my hands are sort of delicate. Girls always tell me that. But I am a little on the fleshy side, and all I need to comb my hair is a wet sponge. Ha ha. You're a hell of a pretty girl, and what's that talk about big boobies anyhow? There comes a time when they drop down to your bellybutton anyway. I mean if they're that big. Not that I'm against them, mind you, but they always get carried away by their own 'wate an' fate.' Ha ha. Now take small boobies like yours. I mean she says they were pretty small. Maybe she was kidding me. How small, honey? Thirty-two A? Gee. . . . You got long nipples or short ones? I like a bite size. Not that I'm going to get rough on you or something. *Always* a gentleman. Never fear. Sheil told you. But laughs are laughs. I can relax with you dolls. And I'm a tit man, deep down, yes sir. Well, as long as they're nice and firm. You can't have everything, can you, and from what I see on that barstool down there, you got some frisky rear end on you, woman, and those legs are something to remember. I knew a girl in Cleveland, she had like ten dimples all over her can. I'd make her walk on top of me, not all over me, mind you, like those creeps you read about, I'm no crackpot, I'm normal, for Chrissake, but I'd lay on the rug, and I'd make her take off just her panties, and keep her dress and slip on, and stand with her legs sort of apart above my face, *and I'd peek!* Lord, would you do that for me? That's what I mean, tits aren't everything. They help, that's all. Not that I need help. I'm one hell of a stud, once I get started. One thing I like about big tits: I wrap a pair of panties around and stick a bit of toilet paper between them, and sort of spank them. For fun. I'm not a nut. Just a plain, ordinary guy. Never a dull moment with me. You like me, I can tell. You finish that drink? I'm not rushing you, honey, but I think that maybe I had enough. We don't want to make things too tough for you, do we? Tim, the check! Where's your jacket, huh? Oh, you have it on? Tim, don't you push that kid around. Give him a break, will you. Good-night, everybody. See you, Tim. Gee, it's nice and cool. That's a nice street, right? We don't have any niggers around here. Not that I'm against them. But there are places where they don't belong. Watch your feet, pussy cat. What did I do with my keys. Oh, here they are. Can you hear Pepper? He didn't have much fresh air today. Sounds like he's in one of his moods. Go right in, honey."

7

April 24th

Barry Lenoir had made the preparations. The fee was set. Everyone would pay for his own: twenty each.

There were three fat, cross-eyed brothers of Jewish-Central European dubious cleanliness, each of them expressing ambivalent doubts about the amorous capacities of the previous one. The youngest, Leo, first to come up, had a chip on his balls:

"You better be O.K., kiddo. I don't believe in that sort of thing, but I don't want the guys to think. . . ."

He was a worrier, with a cause. Ben, who followed, wanted to know how Leo qualified, and let himself come to terms with perverted family pride only after I had gratified his prying by a fancied account of Junior's behavior.

Dave, the third one, was frankly patronizing about both his brothers. He did all the talking:

"You don't have to *tell* me, honey, the poor bastards have a terrible mental block."

I quieted down the whole depressing tribe with one password: *fabulous,* to which I added more lengthy comments, for Ben only, or I would not be here, writing this.

I was visited by seven others, severely stewed, the cream of the crop from St. Louis and vicinity's garment retail business. These jolly, down-to-earth tradesmen buy the right of not having to despise themselves while fulfilling their lusty exigencies with us girls. They load us, by financing our bad deeds, with all the responsibility and future retribution for the shedding of their own misused seed. They err because of our availability and cupidity. The more obedient we are to their depraved whims, the more absolved they feel. They are not far from thinking of themselves as victims of the convenient abyss of shame that is a woman for sale. The merchandise creates the customer, so the customer is not to be pursued by any higher wrath.

After thirty minutes, the phone would shrilly summon us, and, from under my squatting body and disheveled head clutched by a pair of hairy thighs—I wish I could use that nutcracker grip, *my* way—my occupant would answer the downstairs call from the next patient, high on the tales of the Fiddlestein brothers, who had joined the line-up again, for a nightcap, in the cocktail lounge, instead of hitting the sack. They said they would be up again later for a second helping, but they never made it. They were too drunk.

Still working toward my finish, either labially or in the continuous way that would force me to douche again before the next case, I would hear from the other end of the line:

"Hurry up, will you, man, for Chrissake, you been up there for months. I got a hard-on just listening to the Fids. Even Leo is flipping. Thought I'd check with you while you are in the saddle. They say that kid deserves a medal. What do *you* say?"

My score would usually back me up all the way: "I say, Marvin, this is it. When I think of all the dough I wasted in Paris, last spring, I feel like shooting my travel agent. The louse never told me the French sent us the best they got. Right here in old New York." And to me: "Oh yes, baby, that's the spot."

The switchboard must have been wise, as usual, but the St. Louis buyers always spent a nice amount in room service, and Barry Lenoir hinted, while making reservations: "You want our men to have a good time, don't you?" As long as there was no unescorted female unsteadily worming her way to the exit door between two and three o'clock in the morning, not a bit of unpleasantness would be allowed to occur in the establishment.

One of the men, no matter how sleepy, plastered, fucked out, or grouchy, had to take me down to a cab. I insisted on that beforehand. They agreed gallantly when the evening was young, but after the ball had been had, I was sometimes made to feel, by a pregnant silence, during that trip down in the elevator, that I was really imposing. They did not mind parting with their dough—they, too, sat in the mercantile uneasy chair—but that immoral obligation of putting me in a cab, man, it was almost like walking me home, for God's sake. That hurt their ethics, and titillated mine when I had enough left, after being duly appraised, evaluated, and defiled by the EC—elevator creature—man or boy (and this is the right place to tell one from the other), that male who knows, always knows, and lets his stare crystallize on the tiredness under your eyes, that hairpin on your coat collar, the light swelling around your mouth, that stocking seam slightly crooked. The shape of your legs, and the color of your hair are neatly registered and taken note of. He will see you again. He is dying to pimp for you. Once or twice, sent back unescorted despite my insistence, I have replied by a vague and shaky babble of French to some direct ancillary approach and left the lobby, almost running.

On your way up to a job, you may be somebody's girlfriend, wife, cousin, or sister-in-law. You also may be something else, but you benefit from doubt and any accusing gleam is filtered out of those eyes that try to guess and still remain courteous, those eyes that will light up on you, a few hours later, with ribald recognition; "She had to be *it*. She looked just too goody-goody."

After scoring, unless it has been a speedy scene that does not tell on you, you cannot fool yourself into thinking that the EC is fooled. They know when you just got off it. They smell it. Once in a while, it is the John who gets the once-over, discreetly but none the less nakedly, and your share is then a refreshing, forgiving go-home-and-rinse-it-out wink.

At the Commodore, one young, skinny Spanish stud makes me hot inside just by one slow sweeping stare at the middle of my body, as I am on my way up to a party of three old wrinkled mammoths.

Go home, Lily. Go home. Which home? I have only my own seedy self to crawl back to, its folds and creases, its dark musty corners, its smell of defeat. But I will fight for its maintenance—vastly unnecessary as it is—as long as I am alive, unless I decide to part with the whole system. This would be the only free decision I could make, but I am frightened by anything free. To quit with life. . . .

Would it be possible to penetrate into nothingness with the same delectation that escorts my entering into sleep each night? Yes, to quit with life, with that grotesque party I have been made to crash. Nobody invited me, and I never wanted to join the fun in the first place. Leaving is up to me, but it takes balls. The party owns you. You have been had. By the balls. They keep them as a deposit.

A few memories haunt me, more constant and real as time passes: my husband's soft calling of my Christian name, his great expectancies glued on my back like a pair of impotent wings, his faith in me as his woman, his patience and silence in our last year together, pushed to the limits of endurance, the fearful burden of his contempt, fidelity, forgiveness, and magnanimity. From the first days of our marriage, everything was undone, threatened, condemned to death, by that sick knot of fear and guilt gnawing at my insides, warning me, as I was standing, chubby-new and white-clad—o my stubborn-angry fist-tight orange blossom—yes, warning me on love's threshold of my basic inability to cherish, undented by good will, of my refusal to let any son of woman share anything with me other than a mere bed, have anything of me other than a right and a duty.

In my room another anguish swallows me up, as I lie on the bed, scattered with pencils and notes, ashtrays, and those bottles of pills I never swallow—content to press them in my sweaty palms, holding hands with my timid death—the weight of all-alike weeks crushing my chest with clawfuls of opening zippers, flapping belts, gaping buttonholes, men's ties end on end, gigantic numbers and obscene doodles scribbling slimy patterns all over my skin.

One leering cab-driver who wants to buy me a drink.

Salty male hair curls around my wisdom tooth. Strangers' sweat and sperm pour into my skin pores, at the most candid parts of my body: my cheek, my armpit, my shoulder blade. I become allergic to eye make-up, touch-ups between jobs. More indignity is planned, arranged ahead of time, on the telephone. I worry over a tiny growth under the eye which I cannot smooth out; it came for a visit, loved it there, decided to stay. I receive advice from my housewife-girlfriends of yesterday, about how to catch me a new husband. Their children used to come to Michel's birthday parties. An almost unreadable letter arrives from Michel: he skinned his right hand in the school playground. Somebody other than me made him cry with iodine.

One understanding cab-driver who just leaves me alone.

I ponder Ossie's words: "I never let none of them scores stuff me. They'd suck me off as much as they'd want or they'd turn aroun' and let me take care of their bloody piles. I could always think of something else while I was givin' it to them. I'd concentrate on the jack, just like you do. Bread is the humpiest, sexiest thing. Some of those queers would go after sailors only. They made you keep your clothes on all the time, even the cap. I knew the bars where they would come huntin', and I'd tell them right away over the first drink that I wouldn't take nothing in my mouth except gum and that I didn't mind gettin' their crap all over my rubbers but that I wanted to keep mine inside where it belonged, with nobody tossin' it around."

One night, I find the kitchen floor covered with broken glass. Lucky Strike butts betray Ossie's trail. I learn next morning over the phone that I am "a lowdown pig" to use with my Johns the special glass he brought me over as a gift, and for leaving my place in "a state": handbags ransacked, suitcases opened, clothes in a pile on the rug. He assures me: "I don't care if you're a slob. But the way that room looked, I thought you was busted for sure, and I went out of my mind. Then I see them glasses and the empty bottles an' I figure you had a blast."

Then he asks, as an afterthought: "You didn't cut your foot?"

Tiptoeing to the bed another time, holding my shoes in my hand not to wake up Ossie, asleep on top of the blanket, I am stricken by the abrupt certainty that the fiend is keeping his eyes closed and his breathing even to fool me. It had been all planned that he would come up and watch TV here after shooting a wedding in the neighborhood, while I would still be at work.

I lift the corner of the rug, very quietly. I pick up and count the money I hid there before leaving at eight o'clock. One of Ossie's eyes, the one with a green spot in it, pops wide open: "You rat fink, you. You don't trust me none."

"Next time you pretend to be off to Dreamland, I'll slug you, Os, and I will count my money any time I feel like it."

One hotel room's door lock refuses to work. "So what?" fumes my paramour, and he will not be talked out of his spoony designs. I fail to convince him that he should get another room, and I do my chores with an eye on the doorknob.

My masseuse's hands are light and sparing on me as if she knew how soothing a touch I need. She turns me around and over like a doll, taking away from me even the initiative of motion and the necessity to be attentive to her bidding.

One John's turd in my toilet bowl will not go down and I get sobbing-crazy at the funny horror of it: the hell's gadget is stuck, and I would rather fish the thing out with a fork and throw it in the yard than call the janitor, who looks the other way when I go down the stairs.

Housewives on the street shop for diapers, high-bounce balls, coloring books, pipe tobacco, men's socks, and food for those they love, for those they keep warm, healthy, comfortable, alive. At night, they go to the movies with their husbands. They pay the telephone company with stainless money orders, no apron strings attached.

One war veteran cab-driver who tells me all about de Gaulle.

Eddie Krutz keeps me struggling on his knees—he is six foot five and weighs like six horses—while pushing and twisting, deep between my legs, a Coca-Cola bottle— not the large economy size, luckily. Flippy Bruckstein is looking on and swearing: "I lost my bet, Eddie, she loves it." He is not lying, for I became all moistened with need the minute Ed took that bottle from the table, swaggered to the bed, and pushed my half-slip up sharply while Flippy lowered my pants. It happened at the Hampshire House at one o'clock in the morning, and, later, nobody walked me down to a cab, or even to the door of suite 1295. Eddie yelled: "They'd better not give you any trouble in this house with the bills they make me pay."

I trot and limp in the knee-deep snow between the subway station on Sheridan Square and my Village room, on a late December early morning, with no cabs around and a bum following me, as I run and fall and run, with a slit swollen like top sirloin—that's what I call traffickitis—and my legs freezing wet, well above my garter tops—you cannot wear warm slacks and heavy hose on dates. Then, in my room, safe just in time, the bum banging on my window grate, my gloved fingers so stiff that my handbag falls down, lipstick, douche bag, compact, comb, Kleenex, loose change, address book pouring out, *but no purse,* I realize that I must have dropped it in the subway as I was fishing for a token. There were no cabs around because of that sudden snow. Gone is the money I made tonight with a pack of six young hogs who played at spraying one another with shaving cream, breaking things in the bathroom, and who almost forced me to douche with brandy. They started spreading me at the right place, but I screamed so much that they gave it up. It was a private apartment. I had to wait and plead and nag for my fee. They were so drunk that they could not find their pants and jackets. Everything was a mess.

I cannot get used to those weird calls in the middle of the night, as I am just starting to feel the effect of the third sleeping pill: "Come and see me Lily, it's Herbie. I want some comp'ny. What do you mean it's too late? What do you mean you're tired? If you're not in my place in thirty-five minutes, I'll call the police and report you to the little boys blue." Of course he is drunk and will do nothing of the sort, but I cannot go back to sleep.

I nurse the certitude that something definitely ghastly is going to happen any time now, that the Machine is all set, with a diaphanous holy finger lifted to push the button. I pray to that glorified Peeping Tom they call God: "Send somebody to erase me. I was a mistake from the start." Or something like this: "Let an accident happen to me and leave me disfigured and slightly crippled. Then I'll *have to* go back to the Professor and lap up his pity, love, and understanding. Maybe I'll even grow a heart at last." It all ends up with the same loving curse: "Dear God, damn you, please stop doing whatever it is you've been doing to me, ever since I was born."

One cab driver who asks me if I was a voigin when I got married. I tell him I am still a voigin of a sort.

A raping party is set for me by Frankie Casavecchia, in a West-Side apartment, with a few guys who spend their nights at O'Bannon's Bar and Grill on Third Avenue. This is to test my good shape. No money involved, there never was with Frankie from the time he found out about my swinging connections and had a little talk with the fellows who used to have me for nothing. I do a bit of rehearsing with him, first. At his signal, over the second round of drinks, I am supposed to get up and inquire about the crowd's intentions over little me. Then it's every man for himself. For myself.

"But don't snap your fingers at me, Frankie. Nobody snaps their fingers at me."

Bill, a tall albino who was kicked out of a bank; Uncle Coach, former football hero; Sandy, a pouchy tycoon from Sutton Place, who manufactures a wonder car cleaner made from a stolen formula, all held me, kicking, on the bed. I went down twice on the floor with a bang. They finally got the right buttons, elastic bands, and hooks and eyes. Bill sat on my arms, emptying a glass of rye, Frankie labored at my left thigh, the Coach at my right foot, and Sandy screwed me first with the pink plastic monstrosity Frankie calls his "little brother," the one he takes to straight parties in a sandwich bag "for Heroes," just in case: "You never know." Frankie kept inhaling those acrid capsules he breaks under everybody's nose. Blond Bill let go of my arms and turned the TV on. The Coach caressed and poked at my lips with lubricant-wet fingers, forcing me ready for Sandy, in a thick stinking cloud of Amyl-nitrite.

A week later, Cass emcees the same sort of happening at Dave Bernheim's studio . . . I am tied and blindfolded on an ironing board with my clothes pinned up high. The boys tiptoe around me, whispering, giggling, arguing under their breath, displacing furniture, opening closets, splashing water. All those methodical preparations, reminiscent of an abortion room, tickle me funny, and, being ungagged, I start disarming my would-be assailants with a number of jokes that turn everybody off. Released, and wrapped in Dave's old fishnet dressing gown, I make coffee for everybody, while Dave runs tapes of my own frenzied voice, dissolved by nearing orgasm into a sing-song of bilingual bliss. Those tapes stand witness to a past evening of togetherness, with Cass and Dave on top of me and Sheil watching.

I sit with Jerry C. over lunch, at the Delmonico, trying to enjoy a breaded veal cutlet, while enthralling J. C. with wife-spanking stories. He is so feverish that he does not touch his food. I drink his Scotch and eat two portions of pecan ice cream. In his jade-green room on the sixteenth floor, J. C. pushes me into a closet, whacks my bottom with a wooden clothes hanger, and addresses himself to a missing audience. He also plays the part of fictitious supporters, hollering for more caning, and finally uses his belt on my back, buckle-end free, the bastard. Luckily I manage to duck most of the blows. I sit on him just in time. I had foreseen, from past experience, which bull's eye his pathetically tiny ding-dong would select, and oiled it around and inside, so that the mud-bound homing pigeon is not hampered by his usual gaucherie. One would believe that, because of its easy handling and unpreposterous dimensions, this object would encounter no difficulty in entering whatever cavity it endeavored to fill. On the contrary, you never saw such a sly, slippery, unmanageable, unreliable, hard-to-locate prick. Once I have it securely stationed—only by verifying with a discreet finger can I be sure of the fact—I know that I can rest in peace, for the following measures will be quickly disposed of.

This time I do not have to douche. A big push will suffice. J. C. *has* to wash thoroughly. Sixty bucks.

One cab-driver who sighs: "The Delmonico is not what it used to be."

I get crabs from Ossie. It has to be him, with the company he keeps uptown. Not that he's touched me lately, but he slept in my bed twice. I am having my period at the same time, and I stay three days off duty, messing my undies with blue ointment—so sporting the French colors where they fit me the best. Besides, I hate the smell of Cuprex.

I see *The Blacks* at the St. Mark's Place Theater, by myself, in worn slacks and antiquated raincoat. I love old comfortable clothes. I feel a bit cold and unwell, which puts me in the best receptive mood for that seething play. I miss Michel so much my fingers hurt. I cannot push his face away. I will go back to the Professor. I will write to him tomorrow. Or, better still, I will call him. I happen to know he is in Brussels right now. I have just enough cash at home for a long-distance call. If I do not get him, if he's left Brussels, I will write to Paris. I will address my letter to the Sorbonne. They know where he is. They will forward his mail, they always did.

It is the intermission. I call Cass. "Come and get me in an hour or so, Cass, please. I'm fed up. I'll go back to France. I'll start teaching again. I'll beg the Professor to give me one more chance to deserve him and Michel. I'll prepare a show for the Galerie Charpentier. I'll find one of those Jesuits who does not believe in the devil and the original-sin bit, and I'll get reconciled with the Church. Maybe I'll be convicted, I mean convinced. What are you saying about a Freudian slip? Who is Freud? He never existed. Suburbanites made him up."

The play is over. Cass shows up, his shy cat's face shining in the rain. You feel pure, at peace, exhausted by your decision. You will never take a contraceptive pill again. You dream of bringing Cass to the Professor, a chastened, sworn-in Cass who will play rummy and soccer with Michel. Cass understands. Cass knows why and how much your fingers hurt, and he nestles the five of them, softly, in his warm left pocket. You tell him you are too tired and disgusted to paint these days. You are not a whore. Therefore you must stop living like one. Sucking assholes is not a life project. Cass listens. Cass approves. The next day he also approves of your putting up with it all, again, your planning a threesome with Sheil for a hundred each. You never have to tell Cass, "I changed my mind," or present him with any phony rationalizations. So much for Cass. As for facing yourself, all you have to do is repeat one sentence over and over again, morning, afternoon, and night: I did Michel a favor by leaving him. But my little one goes on calling my name in his sleep, and the flame in me flickers and dies: the need to serve, to be good for something, someone.

Strips and tatters from the life of previous years still cling to my daily schedule and make it even more hectic, but I dare not stop seeing that nice Scottish couple who invited me to stuff the Thanksgiving turkey; they do not know what I am doing from twilight to dawn and ask about Michel's marks at school. They used to take him fishing and feed him homemade cookies. I still want to give a worthy reflection of myself once in a while by sitting among a few well-liked former students over the Egyptians' concern with giant birds, the fourteenth-century Flemish painters, and the first Dadaist exhibition in Paris. I still go to art galleries and museums, theaters, libraries, but not any more in the gratuitous, freewheeling way I used to. I take advantage, feverishly, of any slowing-down of my trade, to fit in a few high-pretense ventures or outings. Face it instead of face-saving it: you have to send yourself marching out. You are on duty. The restriction, the limitation contained in that little word "still" is on you. You are "still" aware, but for how long?

"Don't ever snap your fingers at me, Frankie."

A young French waiter with a lispy Breton accent and a slight limp was sent to me by Francine, an old-timer from Montreal. I turned him down a few times on the phone, because he belongs to the "Can I come right now" category. I do not like headwaiters, anyhow; I half feel like tipping them when they leave. He finally made it to my rocking chair on a slow day, sat on its arm for ten minutes, looking me over severely. Sitting still on a rocking chair's arm is pretty tricky. I was fascinated. The little

104

man seemed comfortable and even relaxed, as if he were weightless. The chair did not even creak. I tried it after he had gone and could not make it. I am not weightless.

"You are too tall. Not busty enough. And the wise-guy type."

I stood with my arms folded and glared back: "I am not even *supposed* to be your type. You couldn't be mine if you tried. This is not a marriage agency. So grab yourself by the suspenders and stop wasting my time. Why did you leave France anyhow? What's wrong with it? I bet your father has a farm around Plougastel and that he grows strawberries and artichokes. You are a fine one to look down on me."

His eyes widened and he left, haunted by Brittany's fruits and vegetables, by the sweet melancholy-breeding memory of it, and I felt rejected by the whole species of man, from Adam's daddy to Gagarin's son, and disgusted by my own class-conscious, petit-bourgeois provincialism, undented by so many years of New York cudgeling.

Twenty-dollar bills pile up. A few fifties. I caress my cheek with them. I like the fifties. I carry them reverently to the bank vault. Spending money makes me guilty. Saving it gives me respectability. . . . In the vault, my friend, the old clerk with a crippled arm, tells me about his lumbago, and what this neighborhood looked like when he was twenty-one. He always talks about the time when he was twenty-one, as if he was touchy about ever being twenty.

One cab-driver who gives me eleven reasons to stop smoking, and drives at suicide speed. Nobody makes much sense.

I meet Cass at the Roosevelt on some late Friday nights

after his firm's conference on stocks and things. We stop for a hamburger and a movie, on the way to his place, or drop in at Dave's studio, or take a bus downtown and walk around the Village streets, from bookshop to bookshop. He buys Fitzgerald novels for me, and the latest Baldwins. On the first page of *The Fire Next Time*, he writes: "To Aimée, a best seller in my life." He also selects one Doubleday book, *Tales for Children from Eight to Eleven*, and has a way of hiding it under the others that makes me swallow hard.

Once, we go across Central Park. The air is overripe with red soggy leaves. We share a stick of gum and both stop to urinate all that Chinese dinner's dark tea. The night is quiet and purple. I make my steps longer to fit Cass's. His shoulder is warm. He is dreaming of something. Near the children's zoo, I start crying. In his room, later, Cass just sits there, without a word, while I go on wetting his shirt front.

Mrs. Burns calls me from the college. She asks if I will be able to take the class again next fall. She once picked me out of sixteen hopefuls, because she appreciated my enthusiasm. Some of my former students have asked about me at the night-class office. There is a waiting list of qualified instructors, all ready to fill in for me, but the department is loyal, and sensitive to the rumors about the "personalized approach" that made my class attendance pretty steady to the end—which is new for the art appreciation courses—I wore prim plaid dresses and low heels and was asked to dinner only three times. Not to be asked at all would have been too much to ask. I tell Mrs. Burns that I shall not resume teaching.

One cab-driver who wants my autograph. Still impregnated by Zion's sons, I sign: "Sadie Bitterschmock."

I am invited by a public relations pimp to a party given by a kept chorus girl, Goldie Asters. Newspapermen and beatniks crowd the three small, elegant rooms. Goldie wears embossed lounging pajamas, her hair is matching magenta pink. Cass finds her nerve-racking. All evening he is fluttering by my side, then out of sight, then by my side again, then on the tiny petunia-flowered terrace, two girls toying with his lapels, while I dance with a red-headed reporter who repeats, "Unpalatable. . . . Unthinkable . . ." his eyes on the black linen ceiling. A North African exchange student who lives poorly on two and a half combined scholarships tries to monopolize me. In tense and immune to "la facilité américaine," he has the soulful, caressing look of the Professor and is soon taken over by Cass, who comes to my rescue at the first wink.

A few medium-sized big shots of the advertising Mafia —all of them Johns—are introduced to me by large suave Lester Ferrian, who happens to know quite well aging Firmin, the "Petit Français" representative, whom I visited steadily last year, after teaching hours—he lived close to the college—while the sitter prepared supper for Michel. Firmin was usually critical of my cologne and of my underarm-shaving ways, like most Frenchmen who read Simenon. He made me bite and scratch his balls till he came. I never saw testicles like those: dusty biscuit-colored twin punctured balloons with wide ripples of elephant-tough skin, loosely wrapping an unappraisable amount of jelly-rolling flesh that escaped my touch till some monstrous hardening, gathering, and swelling of tissues brought me face to face with the most freakish subnormality one pair of pants ever sheltered this side of

the ocean. The third piece of that battery was lost somewhere among those bountiful hills. It was not designed
for my tactics by its owner, who had frankly disowned it
and reduced it to a means of last-minute channeling. My
only specific duties were to tend to the mishandling of
the most obvious. That, and only that, lifted Firmin to
paradise.

Cass and I escaped, now and again, to Goldie's bedroom carved inside a mauve powder puff. The phone was
under the bed, and, for ever, a guest, lying on the fur
rug, whispered cryptically between fits of suffocation:
"I'm not drunk, my dove, it's the bearskin."

Cass called Sheil who was swinging on her own that
night. She reported only routine action at Price's, and
we decided that it would not be worth-while to join her.
At about two o'clock, as Cass was helping me into my
coat, a willowy, toffee-colored Negro made his barefoot
entrance and touched my shoulder dramatically: "You
could not be leaving so soon. It is preposterous." He had
a secret, impish smile. I agreed it was a case of tedious
timing, after checking Cass's face in the mirror and reading on it the unmistakable, sleepy, WTR sign: Wish To
Retire. The tall dark shadow bowed shortly: "Fate's paths
are capricious. I shall try not to mourn today."

8

May 2nd

When I am a little drunk with Scotch or sleeping pills, a few dreams come to visit me. Malignant or humorous, they slip back onto my feet the glass slippers of yester-year.

May the Great Witch have mercy on the drinkers who want to forget. I drink to remember. It always works, up to a point, and I take the risk every time.

My Pappy-Phil dream is just as harmless as the ostrich-feather fan Pappy once dusted me with, four of our Host's chaplains, hot beneath the cloth, keeping my body sprawled and very dead under the low, gyrating, unlit chandelier.

One September night, bemused and awed, booted and trousered in black, I was introduced to Pappy-Phil Mac-Moose by his good friend Saul E. E. (for Eager Encore) Cohenz, the gallery owner best known to the "in" crowd by the name Mister Clean. Saul thought just enough of me to bring me as a new recruit to Pappy's kingdom of the Nimble Night. As the sold-out underground fact of my membership became known, a fair number of men started crawling on their bellies at my surprised ankles, begging to be invited to one of Pappy's parties: "Even a tiny off-season summer-stocky one. . . ." But my answer was a cool shake from left to right. No female member could ever bring an escort to Pappy's headquarters. The Prince knew when to refurnish his stable, but he did the picking himself. And his stable would present new girls to his one-man appreciation committee. I was tried, found worthy, and admitted to the tabernacle of togetherness, alone and amidst a gentle crowd of worshipers.

To describe the man, I have first to take one step back from that four-dimensional mountainous error of nature, that geographical challenge of accumulated flesh and weedsy hair playing squatter all over torso, limbs, and face, brushed back shiny, on the rooftop, into a voluminous terra-cotta pageboy which gives countless headaches to cameramen and pushes its possessor's long-suffering tailor to stick to very definite period-style suits, vests, overcoats, robes, G-strings, and velvet Rembrandt head-dresses.

Something godly hovers around the man, a shade of the cassock, a salty reminiscence of priesthood that sits as a triumph of ambiguity, since Phil mostly hates Christianity: "The Death Wish Religion." But he borrows his vocabulary from the sacred texts, uses liturgy to describe his love labors, and has often been known to express himself in parables.

In the candlelit corridors of his twelve-room apartment, uptown, one floor and a half of annexed West-Side Eden, unholy knights in armor, Spanish bishops, and shameless monks chase after joyous maidens, clad in stiff-starched, long-hemmed nuns' undies and their chastity-beltfuls of orgiastic vows.

110

Pappy-Phil favors costuming over all other induce-
ments to an erotic happening. His wardrobe-disrobe room
fits the range of any sweeping repertoire from Elizabethan
and Wild West to the Spaceship and the Nuclearoid.

A deeply ensconced cork is uprooted and ground out of
me. A battling, dying God, named Glenmore, embalmed
with the wine of his own sweat, kneels across my face,
sheltering it from the light with both down-turned palms
dipped in fiery candle glow. Otto the musician, a new-
comer, mounts me. His friend Ingar lets her tongue outline the length and contour of my legs. Another pace,
another ticklish mossy seat, another dewy raw bunch
of male fruit are commanding me to respond as I remain fuming and severed under the freshly discontinued
ploughing. Then my mouth is presented to Glenmore's
renewed turgescence, new words of delirium choked in
my throat by that silencing stem, eased in there by
Barbara's hand. I feel the pearl of her ring stroke my
gums.

The others stand around the bed, poised in the alert-
ness of the bowman between his two last aimings, touching us reverently to spread apart or moisten up or just
fondle, as flowers are arranged in a vase. They cast good-
omen shadows on the silky walls, tasting joy with us,
grateful to see that joy multiplied by the sharing. All the
time, a music box keeps playing under the bed, and somebody, in one of the bathrooms, is anointing a newly
elected beauty, among scented towels, smoking incense,
and the tub's snowy bubbles of soap.

Barbara is after me, her young leaf-soft hands raking
my hair, urging me to rejoice and melt for her, to soar
higher and higher. She describes the deeds for all, anticipates them, blesses them, and, as I sigh and whimper,

111

I see her nipples bud and stir, I feel her breath quicken as she drinks in my feast, taking it in with the hot fluid flowing from my half-opened mouth to hers.

Big Phil, in the next room, grunts and moans mightily. Everybody stops dead and fervently cheers. The timing is perfect. We were losing our minds, all of us, and this is a welcome pause. Every time our Host assesses his potency, we acclaim his name. Phil does not allow any lewdness or dirty stories in his home. We all make use of our passion in a devoted, solemn way . . . I once heard Phil say in a terrible voice, "No disrespect in the Church, please," as a passive participant—there are no "voyeurs," everybody is contributing—was trying a saucy remark.

There is a tacit link between us. We are the flock of precious and envied ones Phil has chosen to set free to oneness. Just by letting us through that door, glittering with chimes, he has turned us loose on one another, every one of us bent on giving much to many, on letting his heart be overcome by what Phil calls, stroking his bangs gently, "his peaceful spirit."

From Pappy-Phil's days it is easy to plunge back farther to the times of my dance-hall addiction.

They say that just the closeness of another body against yours is enough to protect you from the worst anguish; they say that the need for warmth never leaves a sick body. They know what they are talking about. About that quest which drags me to the same little old dance floor, even though the rapture of sex so often fails me: my health has been poor; I have lost weight. To wrestle with Eros on an even basis, I must get those five pounds back.

On the dance floor, where I act out only the posturing and gesturing of closeness, I am refreshed, relieved, rested, my cheek brushing somebody's coat lapel, somebody rampant and cognizant of me, from collar button to neatly tied shoelaces.

When he is all leading power, when I am all pliant availability, there comes a time for the stream of obedience to engulf me. This is my oasis of peace, which nothing can ripple. I am contented with my share: that of a thankful loser. Nothing exists but that magnet pulling my feet where they did not choose to go, but where they will simply follow. On the hotel bed or the car cushions which the dance-floor tactics will lead me to, I cannot relocate in myself that tender zone and have to feed on much cruder hay.

Dear meringue partner, I have my rules and they do amaze you. I will at all times welcome your pulsating maleness digging against me, but I will break my neck to avoid your gelatinous cheek. If it gets too uncomfortable, I gather enough nerve to ask you, up or down from a bad case of stiff neck, if I am crowding you. Oh, fast-working, lean-hipped salesman from Queens, it will only provoke some sample of your wit such as, "I never had so much fun with my clothes on," or "Stick around, baby, my name is Action Jack." It is easy to understand how I would rather have you nicely mute, although sometimes the earthy level of your vocal endearments awakes some very distinct stirrings in that low country of mine. I am aware of the affected way I choose to disguise my thoughts about things that are blunt (and this is as good a rhyme as any). It is like wearing gloves to touch mud. Gloves with holes in them.

Bashful third-dance kissers and hasty pussy bumpers; big spenders at the bar and penny-soda pinchers; college

113

graduates with pimples and unshined shoes and night-club bouncers with even their teeth polished; bloodshot-eyed Irish standing over you like unsteady trees; wiry, olive-skinned Spanish boys with too white shirt collars and ritzy cuffs; suave Jews heavy with watches, rings, gold-coin tie pins, and languid eyes, sold on selling themselves to you in that desperate way they have soft-fleshed, easygoing Italians so very wise in the ways of the female, knowing just the weak spot on your spine and pressing on it in the prick-nick of time (some carrying that sense of timing to the end, some leaving it on the night table or in the glove compartment with the prophylactic wrappers). Who is having whom in whose power? They use you. You use them. You are getting even. So are they. They help you to keep your claws sharp and your complexion clear. You have a fair chance not to be eaten up by those of the jungle pets who are meaner than you. You pay for protection at the highest exchange rate: yourself.

And now I will hush all voices and invoke one of the summer days when Michel was away at camp, two years ago.

Come now, my house, all nineteen floors of it, get out of the night-freezer, you supermarket special, you sterilized meat and pampered bones, lazy to the marrow. . . . At six o'clock in the morning I am sleepwalking on my street corner. Nobody is out but a red-collared black dog and me. Shame on you, my refuse-littered neighborhood for that Sunday dressing-down of torn newspapers and beer cans. I am taking a bus downtown to see Michel, in New Jersey. The Professor is busy snoring, his cheek cuddled against the desk top, amidst piles of notes and half-cigars. It has been beastly hot in town. I am debating with myself now: "Can Michel swim properly? How dark did his tan get? I hope he did not let the Brothers shave all his hair off, did not get poison ivy, did not lose his one and only good hand-knit sweater, did learn the Our Father in English, and stopped picking his nose once in a while."

For two solid weeks I have been fighting, with no spectacular success, an unkind colitis virus. I run to the bathroom about six times every night. The days are scarcely better. I carry on with housekeeping and drawing, teaching at school (I barely make it through the fifty-five minute sessions), and tossing Bob H. around his Lincoln's back seat. I warned Bob, but he said he had caught the toilet-seat rush from me last week anyhow, so we may as well let our customary rush consume whatever strength we have left. I throw up my lunch now and then. It makes me mad when I have cooked it. If some jerk has paid for it in some greasy steak house it gives me mixed feelings of pleasure to verify that I cannot keep down anything that comes from those dogs.

I have seen Wolfgang, my doctor, twice. This man is a pink toy duck, full of cheer and wrinkles. He is seventy-one, Austrian, and a Buddhist of a sort. He says gruffly: "Do something about your emotional situation and your bowels will dry up." He has seen me through a couple of cervix-scrapings, which he unctuously referred to as a "fungus." Too-much-cock-fungus. I like Wolfgang. I frequently break down in his armchair. He gave me a drug that has a narcotic in it. It makes me so groggy that I feel twice as bad, which is an improvement.

In the subway, I think of the husband I have just left at home in a room suffused with the smell of his un-

scrubbed self. We have been married nine years. All that
time he has taken one shower a week. Today is Sunday:
he is going to take his four hundred and sixty-first one.
Approximately. I stopped counting the showers he did not
take and the showers he took soon after overcoming the
shock from the first showerless day of our wedded life.
I was shattered but kept quiet about it: I was a wife in
the old continental fashion. I perfected a discreet ritual,
adorned through the years by additional measures of olfac-
tory protection: getting hold of my nose tightly in the
dark, at the precise moment my lord slips back into bed,
making myself ready for the few drastic seconds when his
feet loiter in the surrounding of my nostrils. It took me
years to find out about the lovely way other men smelled.
No double bed was wide enough, gentlemen of the jury,
to eliminate the threat of those few seconds, except that
firm grip I kept on my aforesaid nasal apparatus. In other
words, I declare that I do not care about the beautiful
soul or mind of someone who does not wash his ass after
use. I know that a number of brilliant Americans hold in
high esteem a number of brilliant Europeans of the past
who boasted of undainty britches. I will say to them, with
due stringency: "Do keep your glittering virtues tightly
buttoned. Maybe if they shine bright enough through the
cloth, they will atone for the sorry state of your backside."

In the bus, my stomach cramps become weaker, and I
manage to ease the pain a lot by controlling my breath so
that I actually fall asleep after a few minutes of riding.
The nausea is gone when I wake up, close to the camp,
on a dirt road with bushes on each side. I swallow a few
more pills and prepare myself for the disappointment of
not seeing Michel right away because we rode past the

bus carrying the seven-year-olds to the fair in Hacketts-
town, and I know Michel was in it. Michel is a natural for
the fairs.

I stretch for a few minutes on the campground grass,
in the shade. Then, in Michel's cabin I meet Brother Eric
and we have a little talk about missing socks and pajama
tops. Brother Eric is about twenty-one, a tall, football-
shouldered, brute-chinned, sissy-voiced Texan. Sensitive-
looking. I give it for what it's worth. I found out that,
quite often, sensitive-faced men turned out to be the most
unfeeling bastards of all. But this is a Brother, so rules
do not quite apply. Or do they? While we are discussing
those vanished pieces of my son's trousseau, our eyes start
a private conversation of their own: his, faintly bulging
and pink-rimmed, tell me, rather salaciously for a distinguished student of Redemption College, "How come you
look so good, with those sex-rings under your eyes and
the lazy-cat walk?" There is nothing forward in the statement. It is just plain curiosity. I hear something else too:
"You are the French one with the red-blond boy. It seems
you could take a lot more wear and tear, and you have
been under the harness for close to ten years. That's just
it: Not squeaky-brand-new, but nicely broken in. Just
ripe." And my eyes tell him compassionately: "You poor
lonely prick, you." It is amazing how tenderly you can
hold against you for a whole minute, just a few eyelashes
apart, a shy, hungry, blond Brother Something.

He said the ladies room was all the way down on the
left, and blushed. I decide to give him a break and keep
my hips from swaying as I turn to leave. The mothers
stand close to the shitting booths, with small children
clinging to their skirts. They talk excitedly, stridently,

117

above the lavatory noises: toilet paper makes its hush-hush sound, faucets cough and choke up, lifted petticoats rustle, and flip-flap goes the rubber girdle painfully pushed down. There are four doors. Two of them stay banging opened and have to be secured by the occupant's hand. The thin margin of privacy left to those proper females is rubbed very thin indeed. But the mothers feel comfortable in there, away for a few blessed minutes from their husbands and sons, the enemy species: men. Behind one of the doors you can hear a mother coaxing her little girl: "Come on, Margie dear, come on." The child whiningly performs, and everybody visibly relaxes. Some big sister starts complaining about Jamie's constipation.

The ladies look faded, sweaty, and tired in their finery: Woolworth's necklaces, polka-dot dresses, pink or blue fuzzy jackets, summer shoes embellished with artificial flowers and rhinestones. What a revenge from the weekly slacks and Mother Hubbards. If I could feel self-conscious, my jeans and striped T-shirt would do it. Droopy buttocks, so cruelly girdled that they appear caved in, bulging veins, creased necks, frizzy hair, swollen stomachs, all the damage leaves room for some prettiness here and there, carrying its flag of victory over lower middle-class circumstances and lowest obedience to the church's good advice about the Papist-Nursery-Rhythm-Method, that limits not and spaces not the family, but does indeed limit and space remarkably Mrs. O'Brien's peaks of marital bliss, to the standards fixed by the Proper Authorities of the Parish.

Some women are waiting for a friend. Some actually come here looking for company. They chat and laugh, reveling in loudness, the stamp of vulgarity. To those females, the smell of this place is so basic that they welcome it as they welcome the milkman's bad breath. The handling of soiled diapers, the daily goal of toilet training, the tragicomedies of bed-wetting and the washing of foul-smelling underwear and their husbands' socks, have deeply rooted in them a growing familiarity with the defecation process and the smells that go with it. That smell announces the rotting of the body of man, the so-called fallen creature, condemned to exude, through all of his carnal openings, decay and waste. Women have a high hand over those mysteries. They give life and go along preserving it. They cling to life longer than men do. They learn to cope with the germ of death that life keeps in limping step with. If you do not see what it has to do with Sue and Doris leaning against the door of the john, happily yakking, because they are in their element, you are not necessarily feeble-minded, but you have started rotting more than you should, that's all: you are immune to the stink of the stuff.

There is nothing wrong with Sue and Doris. Of course, rather than watch them bloom in that manurish environment, I would prefer to see that homey pair lying on a soft patch of grass in the empty basketball grounds, dressed in quiet colors and sensible styles, fitting their unbeautiful bodies, enjoying the sunshine (but not improving it a bit), and keeping their mouths shut (or filled, if need be, with potato salad). But they are mistresses of their fates, and it is quite clear that they are going to stay as long as they dare in their haven, that specific spot of New Jersey State, which happens to be a rather drafty, smelly, ladies room on the grounds of a Catholic camp for boys from six to fourteen years of age.

"Boys must be of good moral character and not subject to the habit of bed-wetting." It is in the booklet, but Brother Eric kept quiet about what happened twice to Michel.

That bus is going to come back from the Fair. I cannot, I will not, pursue the dream. I shall not let Michel's freckles get kissing close. I will go out dancing, or to a noisy war movie, or I will call somebody to come and make sex to me.

9

May 23rd

Let's give it to him: "Not this afternoon, Zack. I'll be busy till six. I'm sorry. I told you a dozen times to call a day ahead."

I put the receiver down. The phone is dusty. How can it be when I am at it all day long? I look around for a piece of Kleenex. What's the use? Dust gets you in the end: dialing finger and phony voice and all.

I think of old Zack and his dreadful humility. He knows he is the only one I keep for a twenty and his gratitude makes me sick. A man should not take that. He is not too well off. He comes here by subway, from his office in Queens, after saving pennies all week. How far down can you bring the price of Heaven? He looks like a sad dog in polka-dot shorts. With him, I fake bliss wholeheartedly, not even sure he wants to fool himself that far. He does not aim high. He just wants to be humbled.

I change the orange bulb for the blue one. I like a dark room, a soft light. I covered the three spots on my legs with thick make-up, but it will rub against the sheets. I also have one purple mark on my left buttock from meaty O'Shea's hand. Four days ago, the President of the

Foundation for the Betterment of Human Relations went on and on slapping me hard, overdoing it to make sure I did not enjoy it *and* get paid for it at the same time. He only half succeeded, and the hundred was still mine. So much for the Betterment of my bottom cheeks. How are yours?

Those capillaries are just starting to show on my right thigh, left knee, left calf. I will get Daniel to pay for a treatment next year, not right now. He just bought me a camera and a heavy gold bracelet. Let us handle with subtlety the milking of that fat cow. The plain fact that he manufactures rubber toys makes a joke out of Daniel. A joke should not be rambled on and on. I can take the way he just lies there on my pillows, like a flabby bovine nonentity, as long as he does not get mushy. While he talks about living with me, keeping me at the smallest cost, I cuddle against his ample belly, looking dense, and caressing two different murder plots.

He is fifty-three, English-born, and the grandson of *the* Lord Nelsh who started a distinguished collection of fire-arms well on its way in the States. Putting a price on the priceless has kept the Nelsh blood boiling for three generations. Daniel's third wife has not a thought for the one to come. She keeps busy rolling around on her plush Persian rugs, having fits, strictly on brandy and champagne. Daniel showed me Mrs. Nelsh's photograph. I was expecting a Clairol blonde with a loose chin. It is a Clairol blonde with a loose chin. . . . She had three miscarriages in four years. She would have been a hell of a mother anyway. Not enough kids are blessed with mothers who had nothing but miscarriages.

Daniel owns a parrot. From Coco, his master has taken

the aggravating mannerism of biting his tongue five or six times a minute. I am sure it is appealing in Coco. I cannot think of a thing I have to do to Daniel that I would not rather do to Coco.

Coco's keeper brings me films for the camera he gave me, bottles of white German wine, the reviews of all the confounded books he wrote on *Children's Games during the Roman Empire*—before he decided to sell his soul to Uncle Sam, the biggest toymaker of them all—and, last but not least, hundred-dollar travelers' checks. I started him on a mere twenty-five because he was sent to me by somebody from Revlon who belonged to that miserable pay bracket. But Daniel's weak spot for me became weaker and weaker and bi-weeklier, and he mentioned a big fat raise, bringing himself to the O'Shea's level, and so supplying me with dreams of dropping the small time for keeps.

I speak French with Daniel to remind him of his long-gone Montparnasse days, and I spoil him with all the tongue service he was deprived of, during most of his fifty years. It seems that his first spouses were not trained in the art, and old Pam, the current one, cannot lick anything but booze from the coffee table, when she spills some.

Daniel has the guts to hint that he used to make her delirious in bed before she started favoring the bottle. I could exchange a few winks with that girl on the subject. He wants to divorce her, out of habit, but she will not give up her mink-topped conjugal barstool easily, and I blame her for it; Daniel is enough to push anyone to gurgle gasoline. She might recover without him.

I am wearing a short pink nightie and black suede

pumps, scratched. I am hard on high-heeled shoes. My eye make-up is brown and I have no lipstick on, for obvious reasons. Being Gallic all over is the cross I bear. My mouth is small and looks sad when not busy. I did not know how to use it till I was twenty-six years old. Today it is in good working condition. So good, in fact, that it keeps me from getting worn out where it counts most. I nourish a firm dislike for my nose. Ever since I became a madonna-profiled eight-year-old, I have kept the said appendix up in the air in a valiant attempt to make it look shorter. My hair droops, flat and stringy because of the rain last night. It will have to be enough for that Westchester meat-packing tycoon I am expecting with mitigated impatience.

I stink of sharp cologne. To be expected from something called "Fever." My throat feels dry and stuck. There were only Pall Malls to smoke last night, and I drank lukewarm Scotch, straight. That did it. I check the props: clean toilet bowl, well-filled paper-cup dispenser, mouthwash on hand; a pile of guest towels neatly folded; everything daisy-fresh ready to help the fussy businessman to unpollute himself between my douche bag and his watercooler.

The striped bedspread hasn't a crease, not kicked around yet. I freshen up, a minute deep into the innocence of things. The blue bulb reflects on my glass-covered drawings. Father, looking like a wearied Baudelaire in charcoal, is gazing straight ahead from his frame at the braided dogwhip curled flat against the wall. I know a look of forced approval when I see one. Dad, you have no choice; I put you there, so go ahead and stare.

Michel's photographs, sad-eyed, merry-mouthed, are

124

down on the linen chest, turned sideways to face the door. In the big boarding-school dormitory (I charmed the hell out of the nun who lords over it and obtained the bed closest to the bathroom, knowing that Michel has to get up once a night), my son is curled up under his army blanket, lost in his stubborn last thirty minutes of sleep. Soon a young, raspy-voiced supervisor with dirty ears will come crashing around the sixty-three cots, calling names and clapping his hands. Michel's nose must be hooked by a wet forefinger, his thumb pushed into his mouth, his face half-buried in his pillow, one leg sticking out on the right side.

Yesterday, Ossie sent up to my apartment two dozen tiger lilies. Once again I am made aware of the funeral-eulogy character of that flower. Ossie himself could not have missed those mud-spattered orange-colored petals, so reminiscent of the swamps. Still, they must have cost a fortune. . . . Blood money, Ossie? I am softly aggravated, faced with Ossie's feelings, a mess of tangled shoelaces that I cannot unknot.

The tiger lilies are smothering, squeezed into a pottery umbrella stand by the closet. Too many of them, too much of me. Like those long stiff stems packed together by sheer force, I am wrapped up, against my better judgment—the worse prevailing as often—in this narrow womb of a room. I keep it dark, so that I do not have to wake up completely. A thick, mellow woven-wool blanket hides the sunny backyard.

Between a few luminous loosened threads, I peek at my landlady watering her garden, a cat at her heels. Such is the world outside, the world of people who grow things. Carpenter Street seems far away.

My bed is pushed into one corner of the room. It crouches there, in its aura of improbable rest and suspended action, vital, wide, faintly creaky when it stops holding its breath, between its cell bars of old-fashioned brass at both ends. I discovered it on Ninth Avenue and had no trouble staking my claim, for six dollars and twenty-nine cents. It took me ten dollars more to persuade the shop-owner to have it hauled up to my place, in parts, then put together. Cass tried it with me that first day. It was noisy. I had my doubts about keeping it just above my sainted landlady's widowed head. It was sheer punishment to be distracted, all the while we were playing, by the counting and evaluating of spring noises and headboard grumbles. A few more points for the Snake (Mister Clean's nickname for and against Cass), who, between Sheil and me, is getting free instruction in whoremastering as a sideline and remains scholarly and boyish about it, all six feet of him and the right impact in flesh, muscles, bones, and various savory substances.

Every time Sheil and I brood about our jobs, Cass points out that our earnings are tax-exempt, and it becomes such an obsession with him that I suspect he found there the one and only reason to be sorry he has to go through life with a pair of balls that cannot be put out on the market.

I returned home at three o'clock this morning, after handling, with some degree of spumante, six lightly stewed middle-aged brokers at a dice game, on downtown Park Avenue. All by myself, with a little help from Ossie's benzedrine—let us be fair, if not righteous. At three-thirty, I was sitting on my bed, counting my dough, adding, subtracting, and feeling more like a tired housewife after a washday than a vice doll soggy-wet with seed. Funny how you never get all that goo rinsed out of you, no matter how much you overdrown yourself, short of water allergy. I treated my own case of it to one more for the road, then fell asleep with my stockings on, the orange bulb burning, and my purse on the rug.

At ten o'clock, I gargled some minty green stuff, answered a few calls on the telephone and promised myself that I would not take it in the rear for the rest of the week, even if it got in the papers. And I would not smoke Pall Malls anymore. I called Ossie. When he heard me cough, he said: "Sounds nice." He was shooting and could not stay on the phone, with two models waiting and Sims yelling at him to make it snappy. Ossie sniffed and suggested that I take up knitting. He said he would call me right back, before the next earthquake, meaning something about Sims I presumed. His voice was thick and shaky. He always protests that he is "CLEAN," in that pleading fashion you use when begging somebody to let you lie a little longer. But on the other hand, how can he work the way he does if he is back on junk? He toils like a horse in that studio, killing more film under him than Sims and Nat put together.

He walked me to that crap game last night, after briefly trying to change my mind and take me to a movie. It was raining. We could not find a cab. He left me alone yelling for one (he hates me when I yell), then hopped out of a shop on silent sneakers with holes, stabbing himself in the eye with a newly bought umbrella. He was holding it too low and messing my home-set hair, but I kept my mouth shut, ignoring the passing cabs, happy to be alive.

127

Ossie was a sight, in sweaty T-shirt, red nylon zippered jacket, and patched jeans scribbled at the knees with ballpoint doodles, scolding me petulantly as usual and smelling not too fresh after two nights spent at the studio, sleeping on his feet in the darkroom. His breath is bitter from rotten teeth caused by seven years of patient suicide. That does not stop me from crushing him against my pillow whenever he flops around it, but he would just as easily sleep on the rug, once he is through hugging me back in his bone-crushing way. This is what dope does to you.

Born to an Italian mother and an Austrian father in a Bronx grocery store spiced with more explosive ingredients than sour pickles, garlic sauce, and stale pumpernickel, he calls himself a mutt. When will he start biting?

I left him in front of the apartment house. There was a green car parked at the curb. I saw Ossie stiffen and smell "the man," his face stormy with a long police record. "It's not them. Man, I'm slipping. When I was a thief, I wasn't making no mistake."

I pull the shades in the living room, empty except for a powder-blue carpet and my paintings, close together on the walls in two, three rows. On the easel, an unfinished portrait of three little girls and one teapot waits for the return of a painter who comes and goes. Mostly goes. Moved by remorse, the wrong kind of inspiration, comparable to what catechism books call "imperfect contrition," I uncap a few tubes of cadmium, and fool around with a mixing of ivory, black, yellow, and red. I try the deep brown layer of paint on the top left corner, where I drew a beamed ceiling. I despair over that background. Anything will kill it. Maybe I should leave it unpainted:

the raw dull off-white linen texture, hardly stiffened by a casein coating, sets off the childish profiles and the bulky outline of the teapot better than any dark finish would.

That dopey umbrella. . . . He brought me, last week, a small expresso machine they must have used as a prop at the studio. And his father's ring: a pathetic onyx-and-gold trinket. And two Emersons, bound in soft leather. The flowers he sent with no warning and no card. The books he left lying around, intent on creating the impression he just forgot to take them.

Calling myself names, I stand in front of the ice box, which is badly in need of unfreezing. I strike blindly at the ice, with a dull knife, my hair falling across my face. I wonder at this strange duty I perform, having at hand a man or two whose function is to enjoy me for free. Will this keep my precious emotions from toughening up too much, which they say eventually happens in my line of work? "Tough" is what I am not likely to become. I am tired of men, even though I seek their touch; sick of sex at the moment I relish it most. And as for those specimens I have selected for my own comfort and reassurance, what they arouse in me is nothing but misplaced maternal devotion, as I worry about their eating habits, missing buttons, the late hours they keep, their jobs, or their not having one. Instead of reveling in unprofessional lust with them, I find myself too often less carried away than I am with the proper customer—rare bird, I must admit—that can be found at my bedside only on an average of once a week with luck, out of thirty or so hours of drudgery.

But let that tool of a man cross my street back to his car and get hit by a truck and I may rejoice, reading the paper next morning, to learn that New York lost a John.

While my feelings for those I call my friends extend so much farther than the limits of my loosely tucked sheets that wherever they may be and whatever hits them, they are not immune from my devoted concern.

Scotch without soda is giving me another of those bad morrows. Affects my memory too. I almost forgot Sheil. She left two messages with my service yesterday. I still have time to call her: Paul Flint will not be here till two o'clock. Sheil and I need each other in business, but the motivations for our off-duty friendship all culminate with Cass. Today we gloat over our complicity, now that we have done away with the case of jealousy-shot nerves Cass first inflicted on us. He was dating us one after the other, making us step on each other's bare toes, in the adventurous way of the chemist who expects great stormy results from the mixing of two potent formulas.

"Debbie" is Sheil's business name. She says it is bad enough to have the map of Ireland on your face. She should know there is not much room on her face for anything else. There lies her strength: in that narrow, expectant, vacant naughty schoolgirl's face.

" 'Allo, dear. I hope I didn't wake you up?"

"Course not, hon."

Sheil favors the name she chose in her weak attempt at call-girl-next-doorism, one door she hasn't crashed yet, and she is so used to being called "Debbie" that she insists on carrying on with the camp even at home, in my new place—there was no room for parties on Carpenter Street—when the gang is there and we are both off duty, shoes off, minus lubricant and reduced to tired face value.

"Got anything cooking this afternoon, Lily?"

Sheil's speech is the crispest thing there is, with a lilt.

While I am telling her about Paul Flint, I try to put a
face on her voice and I picture a toothy, teetotaler totem
pole. Which she is not. She carries her five feet with all
the craft of a bewildered kitten, and she looks overeager
and a bit stricken, unless she chooses to act bitchy, which
she has to do looking up.

She tells me about Dick G., who gave her fifteen dollars last week and promised to send her a check for fifteen more (which he did not). He stayed over an hour
and a half, talked about *me* endlessly and messed her
hairdo. She still had three scores to go, so she put her wig
on, which she hates to do indoors. I gave Dick G. her
phone number: I feel at fault. Therefore, I reciprocate
by complaining about Pete Schwann, a Belgian maître d',
who had the poor grace to say that my Scotch was second-rate and who bit my ear badly, at the precise time
I got him, after seventy-five minutes of hard labor, to the
top of a limited climax. Sheil is responsible for that animal
being added to my little book, so we are even, villainy for
villainy.

"Sheil, I may need you next week, early Monday afternoon, for a party of four. No switching. They want a
show. Fifty each. I asked for more but we won't get it.
So you get your rosebud ready."

She says: "O.K., Cupcake . . ." and we laugh. We look
forward to another of those bouts. It is delicious to fool
thoroughly those you despise, those who despise you. It
is all fake and make-believe for us. We know the ropes.
That tiny space between flesh and flesh, we know how to
secure it, preserve it, giggle over it. As close as our patrons
may be watching, they cannot witness and measure the
accuracy of a caress. We work on each other at such re-

hearsed angles that the onlooker is made to take for granted what he has not actually seen. The sound track of soft moaning noises and throaty sighs has been auditioned many times. We play at perfecting it. We find each other silently shaking hands with a suppressed grin over parts of customers' anatomies whose possessors are not so completely engrossed in voyeuristic glee that they do not also keep their minds on the meter, I mean their wristwatch.

Sheil and I exchange and share quite a few numbers and keep some our very own. There are a few Johns, not necessarily the best-paying ones, whom we try to monopolize, for some time, till our own cooling-off or their need for variety prompts us to surrender them to common use. It is a good arrangement, which benefits both of us. No kickbacks, no arguments, no problems.

We make a good show team, due to the complete lack of physical similarity between us. My tall-average height makes me look like the Eiffel Tower close to Sheil. She has no legs to speak of, while my own limbsy equipment down there makes up for the fact that a brassiere on me is a touch of the whimsical, a wishful thought. As for Sheil, what she cuddles in her blouse is potent enough to block the consumer's view down below. Cass, who once stood between us both for a snapshot, knew what he was doing about achieving a likely image of the perfect couple, plus one.

I have let my thoughts wander while Sheil was brooding about a sixty-year-old retired mortician who takes nude shots of her and insists that she photograph him too, after she has toiled on him a bit and noticeably lifted his spirit. He then takes a bottle of beer in one hand—im-

132

ported Dutch—and in the other the momentary proof of Sheil's talents. He is short, wrinkled all over, and bald. I saw him once, and turned down a second, then a third offer of fun. He pays only twenty-five. Such gorgeous specimens as his kind are known to part most reluctantly with their money. He has a bad heart. That he might soon succumb to his photographic excesses seems like a sensible hope to nourish.

We are running short of entertaining stories, and finally part after a few amenities about Cass, now living with Annette, a pretty social worker who believes in saying kind, tolerant things about us two. Smart girl. Smart Cass, saving on rent and food.

Although I do not allow myself to be jealous—Cass must be shared, as the sun that blesses all—I cannot help feeling pleased when he tells me that Sheil's face looks cheap in the morning. He may say that just to boost my ego, since he has submitted himself, for the past two years, to a continuous exposure to Sheil's face and other attachments—in the morning. But often is the time when I have to dry her tears after Cass has let her see plainly how restricted and glandular is his need for her and how unwilling he remains to put up with her chatter.

Sex between us now happens rarely, as a sort of afterthought. It has been so ever since I caught myself, just in time, slipping into sheer adoration. Maybe it was not love, but it distracted me too much from my own snake pit. No decent self-centered soul likes to search for its nice lived-in dwelling place and find a deserted hearth. And in Cass's apartment, in Cass's pajamas, the said soul and all the accessories to it felt curiously sobered up, one day, with the fleeting unease of incest set free to whisper:

"This is your own blood brother. Put your panties back on, girl."

The amputation that followed was a success, though not commented on, and fierce friendship was born. I know Cass admires me, and I forgive him. When sex makes us one and a half, it is not a pure roll in the clover but rather a gesture of dedication to our common cult: ourselves.

I, too, have seen Sheil's face in the morning and because I found it younger-looking than mine—by six full-fashioned years—the cheapness of it was totally lost on me. I am not jealous of her belly that has no birthmark and her uncapped, pointed teeth, but I begrudge the state she puts Cass in, when she unbuttons the bulging top of her dress and lifts to his clasped hands the kind of face he likes to make love to, before leaving for work in the morning: mouth greasy with red-blood lipstick, eyes painted tastelessly, heavy with false eyelashes, rouged cheeks, all of it smeared and cockeyed through a night's wear and tear.

In turn, who is she to envy me for the silver bells in Cass's voice when he corrects her with a sharp "Aimée," after she has just said "Lily"? Sheil and I have linked hands on that safest of all tightropes: Cass. Once close to breaking our necks, we have now learned the ways to curl our toes, balance our limbs, and hush our heartbeats. As for the worshiping girls with big plans, who cook and wash for him and share what is left of his 10 P.M. to 7 A.M. beauty rest, we see them come and go. In all my years of watching men make asses of themselves, I have never met that kind of unaffected charm Cass can sweep you away with, before you have time to wise up to the strain and loneliness under its nonchalance.

The phone rings. It is Ossie, asking, in a mournful voice (he anticipates a negative answer) what I will be doing later in the afternoon. He will have his sister's car: "What about driving to a place in Connecticut where they have hamburgers that make you forget about food?" I give it a little thought. I worked hard enough last night to be able to call it quits after Paul Flint, without feeling guilty of the worst sin, laziness, that mothers all others. Also I have never heard Ossie rave about hamburgers before, since he hardly ever eats anything, except wafers, with his two daily quarts of milk, now and then a container of lukewarm chili con carne, which he covers thickly with salt, and something very similar to leftover dog food: the Shadduck Special, made of powder-crushed crackers blended with concentrated canned pea soup. He pours salt on all this, not to season it, I believe, but to hide it from sight. He has a point there.

I say I will be ready for him at around three-thirty. He asks whether I am feeling ill. We usually do not meet till late evening, and then the procedure follows a strict pattern: I am exhausted and on edge; he is sleepy; we speak very little. Ossie lights all the candles and the bed-lamp (subdued by the darkest shade I could find), while I stumble across the bedroom, bumping into things and mumbling bad words. He takes out of his pockets half-a-dozen packs of cigarettes and begs me to stop banging on the walls and to keep a civil tongue, et cetera. After a while, he just repeats: "Would you please shut up?" Then he starts courting the TV set: there is a definite hope that I may stop competing with the late late show. The thing is temperamental, works best when you kick it from the side, hug it for a while, then crawl away without putting

135

your feet flat on the rug. There is no antenna left, my moving trip took care of that. Ossie replaced it with a pop-arty clothes hanger. He brings milk from the refrigerator, flatly refuses a piece of my coffee cake, berates me for drinking tea with it. Orders me to stop showing my thighs and to please put something on. He is something of a prude. I had a hilarious time one night trying to pull the sheets off him. He does not want to be seen in his underpants, let alone without—and would not sleep *sans* them either. He sneaks into bed, when he does get in at all, weary of the last candlelight that might allow my shameless eyes to feast on his perfunctory pulchritude.

He gurgles down his milk and, as I start arranging images and moods for the dreams to come, actually planning them ahead and summoning them, stretched diagonally on the bed with my face greasy with cream, I see Ossie down there sitting on his heels much too close to the TV set, smoking Lucky Strikes so drowsily that he burns his beard or rests his elbow on a candle.

"Ossie, come to bed, you know what time it is?"

"Just one more cigarette, sweet."

He will fall asleep like this. The candle will burn down. The TV will stay on. And I will give him hell in the morning.

Each of us has his own reasons for despising himself, and we waste a lot of breath trying to convince each other not to. When he climbs in bed with me, I like to turn my back on him, his right arm encircling me. Most of the time, I fall asleep immediately. Once in a while, I feel something has to be done about Ossie's health and remnants of male pride, and I turn myself on, noisily, till he gets the idea. He knows my preferences and keeps me turned to the wall, or he lifts me on my knees, entering me from the rear.

Ossie knows that I am a self-made loner who would rather be chained to the stake than accept any sort of responsibility. I treasure all the more the stumbling uneasy words that escaped him one night, in the dark. Those words that made him a child again, holding onto another child. When you cannot carry your own weight, why should you burden yourself with excess luggage? That's what I could not help answering to the mutt's declaration of war. Any man who dares name his heart after me becomes my enemy, and ceases to fit my plan of destruction and loneliness. Not that I ever chose that thorny way, not that I ever elected it for my own among others, but there was only that alternative left after trying to live up to those birthmarks that I wear now as a medal of honor. In my husband's house, I was ghosting around like a housebroken corpse. I had to cut loose, reach for the shadows beyond the fence. They seemed so real then. Now that I have crossed that fence it is the house that looks shadowy. But there is no room for regrets: today I am alive. I brood. I fear. I throb and pant. I moan and grieve. I dream. I run. I forget. Yes, I forget. I forget the exact feel of the little bump on Michel's nose, where he broke the bone against a tree trunk, trying a bicycle too big for him. I save myself from despair every time, surviving from rescue to rescue. I had no choice. I protected Michel from myself. I gained the right to dispose of my own losses. The right and the agony of giving up my Michel.

The doorbell rings. I take the phone off the hook so as not to be disturbed and press the buzzer in the kitchen.

I open the door and take Paul's briefcase. I hardly recognize him, which makes my greeting uneasy. He is tanned, a little on the red side. It is always a good thing to talk about, and I start praising his color. He was in Nassau with his family. He got food-poisoning there. I pour some ginger ale for him. He does not want anything stronger. I sit on the orange hassock, the one with a small round hole in it. Looks like a bullet hole. It is only a heel mark.

I stare at Paul's obtuse face. He is about forty-eight, looks well-fed and contented, which shows he thrives even on poison. He wears a pin-striped gray suit, has two children in college, and, in his hand, a hat with a narrow brim. I try to imagine it on his head: no improvement. We discuss things like containers and jars, his business. He makes a fetid joke about canned pussy.

I think of the hamburger I will eat tonight. Will Ossie really have one? Paul's laughing mouth looks like a piggy bank's slit, lipless and ruler-straight. I dream of stuffing it with spermicide jelly. He is not tall, not short, bulky and soft. He has the kind of face I will forget every time to the end of time. He has a salesman's smile pasted over: he just stretches that mouth and freezes, gold teeth twinkling. He makes me wonder who is selling what to whom. Johns sell themselves. I only sell sex.

He is sitting not too comfortably in the fragile rocking chair, politely waiting for me to get to the point. His time is limited, but he will not say a word to hurry me. I take advantage of it and talk about a boat trip I am planning this weekend. He attempts to bring me back to more substantial topics by noticing I wear my hair differently: I let it hang right instead of left.

He makes a crack about my whip up there, and I give

him the "other cheek" story. He foams at the mouth from unhealthy curiosity while I scramble a few more saucy bits together. I can tell the job is half done already. While he says excitedly: "Lily, what a girl you are . . ." I try to find the words he will use when he describes this scene at 5 P.M. in some bar, across from his office, before driving back to Westchester.

I get up with my glass, my fanny peeking from under the nightie's top and walk to the bathroom where I undress. I take the ice cube from my drink and rub it on my nipples. They will not stand out any other way with Mr. Flint. While walking to the bed, I see that he is taking his clothes off. I talk and talk, while he rolls his socks, pushes his shoes under the table, and folds his shorts. For God's sake, maybe he will ask me for a needle and thread to secure this shirt button he is fingering tentatively. . . . Let wives handle the sewing!

I notice he put his hat down on the record player, and I make a grand production out of going to pick it up, dropping it on the hassock, choosing a record, and putting it on: Flamenco guitar solos, the rhythm most unlikely, if I remember well, to fit Paul's performance. Then back to bed, legs crossed, my big feet demurely hidden under the top sheet. I ask Paul about Ruggieri Kormann, an importer of antiques, our contact. Ruggieri was one of my first customers. I had picked him out of the swinging Sutton Place crowd as a possible John. He recommended me to a dozen of his friends. That was the time when my marriage was going to the dogs: searching hounds.

My gentleman caller joins me in bed, and I do not have to stare at his face any more. I think of my husband who never got that treat from me till other men—dance-hall toughs mostly—taught me how. I take care of Paul just well enough to make him come back in a while. I do not want him as a regular. He aggravates me too much. I am not a beginner: I can take my pick. He makes me stop, roughly, squeezing my hips tight and hurting the purple spot. I watch from the corner of my eye the beige cosmetic stain on the pillow Paul first placed under his back in a gallant attempt to keep me from smothering, and as a reminder of what he expected from me, front and rear.

He suddenly lets out a whinnying noise and before I have time to count one, two, three, I am left with wet tonsils. A glance at the alarm clock tells me that the whole pathetic bout lasted fifteen minutes. I resent it somehow. Out of my disgust for Paul, a distinct arousal was shaping up, but the prospect of not having to douche reconciles me to the situation.

"You are working too hard, Paul." It is good policy to act a little peeved, they always bite.

"I'm sorry to disappoint you, honey, I guess I kept away from you too long, you got me so excited."

The record stops to match Paul's timing. I get up to start it again. On my way to the bathroom I put the receiver back on the phone, while Paul rubs his manly chest, trying to remember where he parked his car.

The cold water feels good. I put my nightie back on and more cosmetic on my legs. Paul gets dressed quickly, his face flushed. His eyes have the shifty look that follows relief. He washes his hands, in his shirt sleeves, and I have to hush him up because he talks too loudly from the bathroom. The janitor may be listening.

Briefcase, hat, a playful kiss with clenched teeth. . . . It is over, once more.

140

I yawn, reach for a cigarette, then put it down and start straightening up the room. The doorbell rings. It cannot be Ossie. It is too early and he always calls first. Maybe Paul forgot something. I run to the closet and reach for the first dress hanging there: a new tweed coat-dress with long sleeves.

I ask through the door, "Who is it?" A muffled voice answers, "Paul." As I pull the door open, just a crack, my eyes kept down, I see four big shoes, brown. The brown shoes of the Just.

10

Up go my eyes, wearily, to the expected sport jackets and open shirts, one of them a loud plaid, the other greenish with stripes, every stitch trying hard to fancy up that unmistakable plain-clothes look. They might just as well have had badges pinned all over and novelty handcuffs pierced through their ears. The faces match, one forceful, the other roundish and guileless.

The law stands in my kitchen, four feet away from me. When did I close the door? I cannot even remember walking from the doorstep behind them. Here I am, the ribbon of my nightie caught in the front zipper of my dress, my hands clasped behind me. I still say dutifully, "Who are you?"—as if they might answer, "Santa Claus and his helper." My heart beats so loud that they must hear it.

This has happened many times in my half-dreams, during those dragged-out minutes when sleep is close enough for my mind to push away the possible nightmares, by sorting them out and acting them in advance, so they will not come back with the greater potency of the real dream. Now, I cannot believe my eyes. This would be too repetitious. Life is not like this.

They are both beefy. They look stern in an amused way. They must have said, "We are police officers," but I do not remember hearing it. I see the badges they pull out of their shirt pockets: they have a way of showing it briefly, sideways, like the dirty picture it is.

"We had a little talk with your friend downstairs. We are arresting you for soliciting, and lewd and unnatural acts."

I will keep quiet.

"Paul is just a friend. We are not intimate. I am painting a picture for him. Look at it, it's in the living room."

They can smell fresh paint from the kitchen. The paintbox is open and a few brushes messy. This should be a break. All they tell the artist is: "So you deny that Paul Flint paid you twenty-five dollars for a blow job?"

They stand in front of my easel, also look at the Crucifixion on the opposite wall, try to make something of it and give up. They walk to the bedroom and stare at the crumpled towels, the glasses, the bedclothes pushed back, the bills Paul left on the table.

I ask shakily: "Were you following Mr. Flint?"

I get the whole story: "We were watching your apartment from across the street. We got a letter telling us about you this week. You are in trouble, young lady."

Who did it? My landlady? The two old women up there who practically live at their window and see men come and go? My janitor, who does not say hello any more? That dirty Lorrie, who promised she would get me because of Jim?

144

I must remember what Ossie said about cop trouble: money. Handed the right way. I look up at them. They are messing around, paying no attention to me, opening closets, fingering records, misplacing cushions, peeking under the bed. They are going to see my bags, right under the table, half hidden behind a straw basket full of magazines. The big round black patent one I take to hotel rooms, stuffed with douching kit, make-up, lingerie, and spare stockings. The other one, a light pigskin tote bag with my passport in it, keys, mail, receipts and bills, checkbook, rollbook from college, *and* a telephone-address book, worn out at the corners. This is what they are looking for.

I think of that game little girls play of searching for something hidden in a room, with shrieks of delight. You "freeze" when you look too far, you "burn" when you get close. They are "burning" all right. They have it.

There are all men's names in there. Quite a few are well known by the vice squad as Johns. They are the most generous and prominent ones who do not see a girl more than once or twice and get to meet all her friends. Those names may be scribbled in more than ten thousand little books in Manhattan. They get around: "Have you got J. A.'s number, hon? No? Listen. I called him a second time early this year. I gave a fake name, a fake contact, and made a date. I wore a black wig. He never recognized me. You know, I lost some weight. Maybe I'll do it again next year as a redhead. If you want the number, it's O.K., honey. You know he's a yard (one hundred dollars). I'll take twenty-five."

The big cop closes one hand, greedily, around the green book cover. With a thick, sausagelike forefinger and a crooked thumb he just goes on turning the pages, whistling softly: "A hot, hot little book."

I almost yell: "Give it back to me! You have no right!" They turn on me, cold eyes shining. I crumple back on the hassock. I know what it will mean to me if they take my book away. The big man puts it down on the table for now and keeps his fist on it possessively. He says: "We are very patient with you." But he ignores the hand I extend toward my book. I try to work on the other one. He is blond, with an easy chin and a puffed-up look. He is staring at that pink ribbon stuck in my zipper, while the big one repeats: "Get dressed. We're taking you in."

The way I jump around, pleading, from one to the other, it must be plain to them that I have no clothes under my dress. I think I catch a glimpse in their eyes and I sit on the bed, fooling myself for a while into seeing a way out. My back turned to them, I start fiddling with my collar and while they get nearer to look me over, I change into a skirt and blouse, pulling the skirt up under the tweed dress and unwillingly dropping the blouse down, enough for them to see how small I am up there.

The blond cop stands close, breathing audibly, the big one pulling at him. They whisper in each other's ears and the game starts, the big one saying that I am not sensible and that we cannot get any place as long as I am crying and carrying on like that, the younger one telling me he is doing all he can to change his partner's mind about taking me in. Each of them takes turns pacing around the living room while the other argues with me in the bedroom. At times they start whispering again together, which makes me all the more frantic.

I try to make them accept money. I only have two

hundreds left. I put the bills between the pages of a book and push it into their hands. They have a way of turning it down that makes me understand they might settle for more. This is not enough. I talk about getting more tomorrow, with not much hope. Those things must be done on the spot.

Ossie calls. I just mumble, "Something is wrong," and hang up. They question me: "Your boy friend? What does he do? Were you waiting for him?" I hope he will not rush here right away. All he needs is police trouble. Two Johns call, one after the other. Then it is Daniel. He sounds mean because he thinks I am busy. The beast. . . . His money would come in handy now, but I dare not involve him.

The cops are impressed. I ask them if I can call someone for advice. They say: "Go right ahead." I try the office number of a congressman-backed lawyer I nearly got mixed up with, through that half-baked public relations pimp, Max Shapiro. I am relieved when a feminine voice informs me that Mr. Koplan is in Brazil. He was supposed to be worse than the Law.

Ossie calls again, to announce that he will be there in a few minutes. He cuts me short. He smells what is happening. The cops catch on and express satisfaction. It is clear that they want to handle this with somebody else. Ossie will be here soon, he has only a dozen blocks to go and I know how he can run. I start to quiet down. Ossie will know how to talk to them. They will not take me away.

They ask for ginger ale. I am drinking the little gin that is left. They take turns in the rocking chair, leaf through magazines, look at my photograph book, where they find the one and only nude shot I have of myself, taken by Jim in a sunny thicket, on the side of the road from Boston to the Cape. I get wise just in time, grab the snapshot out of the big cop's pocket and tear it to pieces. They laugh good-naturedly. They take my camera out of its case and open it, while I wait for Ossie's steps on the stairs.

The blond one makes faces at me and rolls his eyes around. What does he think I am? A kid? I end up laughing piteously, with my make-up running. "You got a hot little book there, honey, you must be quite something."

Ossie comes in with his key, squeezes my shoulder briefly, and walks to the bedroom with the big cop. The relief of seeing him makes me turn weak. I lean against the kitchen stove, my stomach tossing around. The blond cop whispers in my neck, complaining that, with my red-rimmed eyes and face, I am not the same girl who opened the door to them an hour ago. I spit in his face mentally. Ossie comes out of the bedroom, tells me to stop bawling entirely, wash my face, comb my hair, and take it easy. He adds that they have to take me in. He is going to find me a lawyer and get me out of jail tonight if he can. They are not taking my book with them. They pocketed the two hundreds, after all. Ossie must have been persuasive. He drops the book inside his shirt, winking at me.

I put on a coat, grab a handbag, and follow the cops, leaving Ossie home to comb the house for more little books. I have two discarded ones. Ossie will find them in my Philadelphia-bound suitcase, with my whips, leotards, net stockings, Halloween masks, starched aprons for playing maid, and frilly undies for male-petticoating.

It is four o'clock sharp. The cops tagging behind, I

walk along my street, hidden behind prescription sunglasses, feeling conspicuous. I sit down between them in a green car parked at the corner. I think of Ossie last night, sniffing after "the man" on Park Avenue. I think of Lorrie's loving words over the phone, "I'll get your cunt some day," or Jim's concern, "This neighborhood is wrong, Lily"—of some of my Johns' warning, "Your phone number is all over town."

We stop at the Fourteenth Precinct House. A big building with dingy rooms full of men in uniforms, busy in a lazy, ostentatious way. I am watched by all with a careful look that anticipates a second meeting. The big cop—they call him Saul—fingerprints me. I get greasy black ink all over my hands, under my nails. He takes my fingers, my wrists, drops them, motions them, as he would do to a child. I let myself flow easy. I am a thing. I belong to the police. They take me to a washbasin behind a door. They gives me a scratchy piece of soap—not advertised on TV —and a towel. While I scrub my fingers, keeping my head low, a cop barges in, steps back and I hear him ask Saul: "First arrest?"

I am made to wait in the entrance hall with the blond cop. I try to turn my back on everyone; I keep spinning left and right as more cops pass by and slow down. I finally choose to face the American flag propped up high on the wall, and wait to be thunderstruck. Nothing happens. I know I can handle Uncle Sam any old day.

Back to the car with my escorts. They are talking shop over me. They bought me a pack of Kents and drop it in my lap. How kind of them. They have only one hundred and ninety-nine dollars and sixty cents left. The car stops at the Tombs, where Ossie used to have a favorite cell with his name carved on the wall a few dozen times. I am led into a small room, full of cigarette smoke, where a matron sits at a desk, sipping Coke and looking bored, a pencil behind her ear. Two younger policewomen are standing by; one is filing her nails, the other unwrapping a piece of gum. The cops crack a few jokes about how hard some people have to work for a living. They introduce me as a prost and leave. Their day is over. "See you tomorrow in court."

I am made to part with my glasses and my handbag. My money is handed out to me. I put it in my coat pocket. The two girls take me through a door that leads to a long room where barred cells face each other. About seven or eight on each side.

I am asked to take my clothes off. I step out of my skirt, unbutton my blouse. Those young hacks are still green and their voices unsteady. It is not hard to think of them as nurses. The illusion vanishes as they say:

"Your bra and panties too."

They make me bend over to look in my rear for junk. While I am obliging, once more blinded by tears, I see that only one cell is occupied and that the prisoner, a tall Negro in a green dress, is peeking at me and yelling something I do not understand. One of the policewomen, annoyed, makes me lean back out of sight. Feeling gorgeous, I put my clothes back on, intent on hiding my face, and follow the matron into the third cell on the right.

This is it. I jump as the door bangs shut. I never heard a key make such a loud dragging noise as it is turned to the side twice and pulled out. The bars shake and hiss from top to bottom. I will not stay here more than a few hours. Ossie will get me out soon. My lawyer must be on his way.

It is a narrow cell, dimly lit, with a wooden bench on the left, a toilet seat without a lid, a washbasin in the back. So this is the place of indignity in which the righteous seclude the guilty. "We're going to take you in." I try to feel depraved and fail. I sit down on the bench. I am wearing black patent shoes from Saks, and my new turquoise coat, payment of an obese young John called Marshall. He manufactures good clothes and never gives cash. Marshall the impotent. He should be in here with me, with Paul Flint and Sad Zack and Midnight Special and the Ablutionist and big O'Shea and Schwann the Shark and the retired mortician, and all of them. Why don't they ever go to jail? Why isn't it a crime for them to buy what we get arrested for selling? "We had a little talk with your friend downstairs."

The girl in the green dress calls me: "Hey miss." I stand up and grasp the bars with both hands. She has the first cell on the left and I must turn sideways to see her.

"What are you in for?"

"Prostitution."

"I thought so. Like most girls in this joint. They got a few downstairs. It'll fill up soon, you'll see. I'm glad there's somebody to talk to. I see you comin' and I says to myself: 'This girl is shook up bad. . . .' First time busted, for sure, I ain't wrong?"

"Right."

"I been here for hours. They nailed me in Bloomingdale's with a hundred and fifty bucks of stuff. The cutest sweaters and slacks. You should seen them. Only the best. I don't bother with no crap. I been arrested once last year, but I was found not guilty."

She is not a hooker. Grand larceny. That's class. She says her name is Marie. Her mother is from Martinique and she nags me into humming, "A la claire fontaine, m'en allant promener, j'ai trouvé l'eau si belle que je m'y suis baignée." She only knows the tune and wants to learn the words.

What am I doing here, teaching French to a tall black-faced thief, both of us leaning against bars? It is almost like teaching night classes. Only more fun. I look at my feet and see a roach. I step on it, coolly. I am not prepared for the crunchy, creaky noise of it under my sole. Marie retreats to the back of her cell. I hear her push up her rustling skirts and urinate. I sit down, my back to the bars, my knees up. I see another bug. It is part of the treatment. My face starts puckering up, like an overgrown baby's, and the corners of my mouth go down. I cry without tears, pushing my nails deep into my palms to stop, stop, stop. . . . I keep it as quiet as I can, but I hear, over a loud faucet noise:

"Cheer up, Frenchie, first arrest, they got to be easy on you."

I mumble something about immigration trouble, a plane ticket for France, a husband who has already too much dirt on me, a new visa to get, a sugar daddy who may turn chicken, and a ten-year-old boy waiting for me back home. It just keeps pouring out. I would babble it to those walls, scribbled with awkward phalluses, to that toilet bowl. I hate myself for that untimely leaking.

The beaming voice, again: "Lucky girl. Kids are swell." Then, she adds, out of some private failure, "But they are a pain, too." I wish she would shut up. Now she yells: "Matron, matron, may I have a glass of water?" She repeats it four times. In good time, I also get my own paper cup. Marie informs me that most of the girls piss in the washbasin and "she ain't gonna drink anything that come out of that faucet, no sir."

The young matron looks at me with troubled eyes. What is she seeing in me that upsets her so? Like Marie she says, to no avail: "You shouldn't worry too much."

Marie is pacing her cell. She is bored. She wants to know about my schtick. Inner instinct prompts me to be vague. She still gets the point: "You mean you don' have to do no 'hooking?' Tricks call you? You have like a reg'lar clientele? Gee whiz. . . ."

She gapes at me admiringly.

"We are arresting you for soliciting. . . ." Paul Flint called me twice in the morning. He wanted to come up right away. He said he felt tired and could sleep in my bed for an hour or so, till I was ready. I said I did not rent my bed to be slept in. He laughed: "O.K., honey, let me come up at one o'clock, I won't keep you long, honest." I should not have opened the door. I knew damn well Paul had not left his breeches or his briefcase behind. But they would have kept ringing till the janitor opened the door downstairs. Why didn't I have more cash with me? Because I put seven hundred in my bank book last week. You must not keep too much cash at home. But you still must have enough for the police. How much is enough? How many "yards" will buy your way out of that trip downtown?

"Get dressed, we're taking you in." "Are you denying you are a prostitute?" Maybe my skinny top turned them off. Oh, to have Sheil's tits in that kind of emergency. . . . They needed to look at the names in my book to convince themselves that I was something after all. You know . . . French. I was bawling all the time. Not glycerine tears.

Even cops do not like a swollen nose on a girl. This is not the movies.

"Let me come right away, Lily, please. You know it won't take you much time to make me flip." Yeah, just about as long as it took him to spill the beans. He said "please." I felt like painting all day. I did not feel like blowing any son of a bitch. I am afraid to turn them down when they are too horny. They never believe you when you say you are tired. I will not eat hamburgers with Ossie. I will not cruise on Daniel's boat this weekend. Not that I care. Yes, I do. At least he does not raise roaches on deck.

"We're being very patient with you." The blond one had a gold tooth in front, like Paul Flint. He kept feeling it with the tip of his tongue. Maybe he has children. Cops are like rabbits. I remember snatching my boy's photographs from their hands. Why did Paul have to talk? No guts, that's why. The swine . . . I wish I could bite his balls off. Some mouthful of nothing. I wish he was made to spend sixty-nine days in jail and forced to piss in front of everybody in one of his cans.

"What is your boyfriend doing?" Did I mess things up for Ossie, involving him in this mess?

I can still hear the way the blond cop laughed when I pulled my knees together, conscious of his staring. The police have a right to know what is going on between your legs. I curl up on the bench, wishing I could hide in my mother's cunt, but she never had one.

Marie is asking me for cigarettes. I throw her a few and I see her long fingers grab them through the bars. Her hair is teased high, her dress is brilliant silk. She looks more like a hustler than I do. But she isn't. She has twenty-five cents on her. I buy us sandwiches from the matron: tuna fish for her, ham and cheese on rye for me. I'm not hungry, but it kills time. I chew slowly. Marie makes me sing some more, between mouthfuls. The matrons listen. At my request, one of them calls Cass's number with the message: "Guess who is in jail?" She comments, adequately:

"Keep your sense of humor for tomorrow."

She comes back, pleased: "No answer." Cass must be deep in social work with Annette, the louse. I wish all my friends were in the clink. Then I despair over my own nastiness. Three cigarettes left.

Do I see a key in the matron's hand? Is she really opening my cell door? Is it me, following her, unaware of Marie's good-by? Am I going to see Ossie, beaming at me behind a desk?

It is not Ossie. But two cops. Unbeaming cops. They say: "We are taking you to night court." I am so stunned that I can find no "buts" and just walk behind them into a police van. It is dark outside and cool. I hear drums. Puerto Ricans live near. I smell hot sausage. The younger cop wears a paper daisy in his buttonhole. His cap is pushed down to the back of his head. They both walk like hoodlums.

I am sitting close to the open door. I let my head drop here and there all along the bumpy trip. Happen what may. This is no time for worry. I am taken in charge. I ask for the time. It is nine-thirty. They offer me gum. I wring my hands and they turn around, scowling: "You a junkie?"

They talk about missing papers, and getting fouled up, and who the hell is responsible. The minute I realize they

155

are not too sure what to do with me, I start panicking. For the past years, there has always been a man around, to drive me some place.

"Soliciting and obscene acts," of the kind every judge tries to get from his little old lady, on Saturday night, and if she will not oblige, there is always somebody around in court with a hot number or two.

"Obscene acts. . . ." It does not fit that calm evening ride through the Village, my neighborhood of yesterday. The square is aglow, the sky deep blue against thick trees. The cops discuss me: "She won't do it again." And they laugh.

It is hard to believe: they fingerprint me anew in an empty hall where my escorts get yelled at by a plain-clothes vicious-looking spic who has me photographed, with a number around my neck. Necklaces cramp my style; I have never liked them and my face shows it.

More standing around in mildew-smelling lobbies. I keep sweating and shivering. I am afraid to be left here in a cell. Dear God, make them take me back to Marie. The Occasional Listener hears me. I walk with the cops to a smaller van, through four or five blocks, getting plenty of attention at street corners, where Spanish-idle families, slumped on stoops, follow me with knowing eyes.

I need a drink, not of water. Back into my cell. Marie snorts: "They do that all the time, pissin' gasoline away." I drink some water, filling my paper cup at that ill-reputed faucet. Whatever I may catch, I will make it my private business to spread it all over town after they let me out.

The matron comes back to me: my lawyer is here. They leave us alone. We sit in front of each other. Across a desk. He is a young thin Italian with the greasy hair and soft eyes I know so well. Ossie sold him on the case, and he says he will do his best. He tries to humor me by grinning over the fact that so many of his colleagues have to defend ugly old twentieth-time offenders, and that *he* is lucky tonight, even though he was dragged out from a nice dinner party, by hysterical Ossie. The cream of the Bronx.

Yeah.

His name is Enzo Crezzione. He looks worried. He is going to ask for a postponement tomorrow, then, later, plead "not guilty." He hopes Paul Flint will not show up in court, or that, if he does, he will invoke the fifth amendment. I will get out on bail tomorrow. It is too late tonight to get anything done. He will see me in court. I should try to sleep. Do I have a blanket? No? Too bad. Oh, it's not a regular cot? It's a bench? What a shame! Do I have cigarettes? No? He will get me some. Do I have money? Good. Ossie is outside. They will not allow him in. He sends his regards. I say, *"His what?"* and Enzo gets red in the face.

I am back in my cell, my head ringing with words. A few more from Marie. She says:

"You sure travel a lot, tootsie."

Two facts: I have to stay in here all night. And that tango dancer, named Enzo, sounds as glum as Lent.

The matron refuses to let me have the sleeping pills I carry in my bag. The contraceptive pills too. Since I forgot to take the pink pill yesterday, and was figuring to catch up today by taking two, there is a good chance I will be bleeding tomorrow and not a chance I will close my eyes tonight. More water. I sit on the can, then get up.

I cannot urinate. I walk around four steps, turn down, four steps, turn down.

"Get the lead out of your pants?"

The hell with Marie. Let us settle down on that nicey-nicey park bench. After all, it's just a cell. With walls. Like a house. With people in it. Marie and me, the girls downstairs and the hacks, we are people. We must be. If I close my eyes, I can pretend I am sitting at home. I *can* pretend. I do it all the time. If I open my eyes right now, I will scream. Count to ten, slowly. Easy does it. Why did I have to throw Marie six cigarettes? Of all the stupid things. . . . Enzo said he would get me some.

I call: "Matron!"

Marie says, after a while: "The bitch love to feel needed."

Two girls are brought in. Marie jumps for joy. I hear them take their clothes off and put them back on. The matron does not have to say: "Bra and panties too." They know. The aura of recidivism is on them. One goes in the next cell on my right. The other just in front. They are both Negroes and thirtyish. Marie greets them buoyantly. She knows one of them.

"Well, Sue, what's new? What's that brother of yours doin'?"

"He just got out. Ain't that a shame?"

You cannot help wondering where the shame lies: in getting out or in ever being in.

"When were *you* in, last, Sue?"

"I did five weeks in the House, starting February. Same cop got me this time. I can't even turn a trick no more. They grab me doin' nothin'. I hain't seen no money for weeks. I eats at my sister's at night. Things is gettin' worse alla time."

158

"That's what I heard."

My next-cell neighbor speaks through her nose, in a whining, weary way. Marie tells her, gesturing to me: "Hey, Sue, give a smoke to Frenchie, too. Next to you. She hain't got none left. Hey lissen, she don't hook on streets like you bitches, she do it through the fucking phone."

It is said flatly, as a fact. I see a brown hand on the side, reaching for me with a Pall Mall, clutched between two nail-bitten fingers. I take it. I do not thank Sue. Marie did not thank me. That's the way it is done.

The chubby girl in the cell across from me is a small, sulky, very light-skinned grade-C egg, in dark tweeds and soiled sneakers. Her left arm is in a sling. I turn away as she sits on the toilet bowl, scowling at me. Marie calls to her and she does not answer.

"Leave Bess alone, you chatter-snatch," says Sue. "Her man is sick. She got trouble enough without your fancy talk. You ever heard about Mad-Rat Cliff? That's him."

When I turn around, I see Bess lying down on her bench, eyes open, breathing unevenly.

My knowledge of Ossie's turn of speech helps me understand Marie and Sue, who are now discussing the devious ways "the man" has, these days, of hunting every decent hooker on every street corner.

"You know the bar on a Hundred-forty-sixth—The Three Barrels they call it now. Used to be called Old Luke. You should have seen it last year. Your cousin Lucy was a regular. I used to turn three, four tricks a night for three bucks each. I won't go near no more. It's all plain-clothes looking more trickier than tricks. Jesus, do they fool you!"

Four more girls are brought in. I hear some fighting.

159

They are all much older. I cannot think of any cat dragging that in. One light Puerto Rican with limp hair, dyed red, gray scalp showing through, is dragged kicking to the last cell on the left. She wears a dirty pink sweater with sequins. Ugly blue veins stand out on her legs, half an inch thick. She stamps her feet, her stomach stuck out, her eyes glassy. She is sky high on something.

"So old Anna is still around?" breathes Sue reverently as an enormous Negro with a booming laugh enters her cell, with the easy grace of the very fat. At the way she greets everybody, you can see this is home for her. The new matron, a gawky blonde, bespectacled, tells her, "Anne, not you *again!*" with something close to affection.

"It's the las' time, I'm tellin' you! They won't catch me with men no more."

"Yeah, I'll bet . . ." snaps the matron, pushing the cell door shut. All the girls start kidding Anna about her age. Anna protests that she ain't got no wrinkles, not on her face, not anywheres.

I am stunned. Everybody around me is settling down to sleep. I am the only one jumping up and down. The other restless one is Marie, who got permission to keep her transistor and plays it with gusto, explaining that breach of etiquette by bragging: "I'm not a prost."

Some of the girls do not know it yet.

"Oh, shit," says Granma Anna. "You're just like the rest."

Marie argues, without meaning it much, that at least she don't go around, sucking you know what, but everybody has lost interest. A voice asks: "Anna, what about Francine? She got her baby yet?" But Granma is on her way to some childish Eden.

Soon all I hear is snoring from most cells except Marie's,

where the Beatles are taking over, *mezzo voce*. The matron rushes in, like in the famous ballad, and fights with Marie. Marie turns the Beatles down a bit while the matron stands there, then back on loud after she is gone. One girl whimpers in her sleep. Another crushes something down with her shoe and swears. Marie snaps her fingers. Sue knocks her head on the wall and turns around. The girl across from me, Bess, sits up in a soft motion, feels her bandaged arm and stares at me, stroking her bare feet with her good hand. Suddenly she sticks her tongue out at me, and I cannot help smiling back. She just gapes there, for a minute, looking disgusted, then turns her back to the bars.

The Beatles are killing me, but if they stopped, it would be worse. I alternate pacing on tiptoes, drinking water, lying down, punching my stomach, perching on the bench, trying to urinate, exploring the inside of my shoes, buttoning and unbuttoning my coat, biting my nails, groping for the part in my hair and asking Marie for the time, every half-hour.

The blessed matron shows up at last with Enzo's cigarettes. She thought she would find me asleep and scolds me for being up. I thank her abjectly and I see her face stiffen as she notices my skirt and coat. . . . A woman is a woman. I make the purely intentional mistake of asking her for a blanket, just to check on her retort: "What do you think this is, the Ritz?"

Marie sings out, later, in Calypso, something about the matron's private parts. Hours go by. I smoke all the cigarettes Marie does not bum from me. I can hardly swallow. I feel the rings under my eyes, pressing down through the skin.

"You're not the same girl that opened the door to us."

161

You bet your slimy life. . . . Drunk with fatigue, I try to fall in love with my present commitment. I try to reach out for the hands of Verlaine and Villon and Sade and Wilde, who once clasped their own cell bars. In anguish, I strive to think of jail as an island, a neutral shelter. I even remind myself, somewhat untimely, that, one day, I will laugh at all this. I fail in all my efforts of self-justification, dramatization, sick humor, and can only sign allegiance to a mere promise of survival that may extend to the next ten minutes, then, again, possibly, the next following ten. As long as I am not alone. As long as I hear, around me, the snores, the groans, the screams, the toilet noises, the curses, the jokes, the summons for a smoke, of the girls I belong with, with a few bucks' difference between us. I beg them, silently, to wake up.

I start bleeding at around four o'clock. There is nobody to hear my "I told you so." I take my panties off, stuff them between my legs and lie down on the side. My bladder hurts. I doze off a few minutes, with the weight of Pappy-Phil MacMoose on my chest. Then the Beatles call me back to the challenges of reality. I sit down, bathe my face in water, finally urinate with much pain. I have blood on my skirt, on my slip, and down my legs. No soap.

11

May 24th

It is dawn. Light has gained over night another fugitive
victory. Here, the stabbing white disk of the bulb atop
every cell has not flinched. Time, man's helpless response
to the sunrise, works its cruel wonders on all woozy eyelids, and a few girls start yelling for sanitary towels.
Although I am not one of the loudest applicants, I get
my fair share: two pink and white cellophane-wrapped
Kotex napkins. I keep one for washing myself. I stink. I
rinse my panties and my slip in cold water and wring
them as dry as possible. I put them back on, clinging wet.
Marie passed the word around that I have money and I
pay for coffee and doughnuts.

As I watch the girls gurgle and chew voraciously, an
alchemic backfire of glandular sympathy fills my stomach
and moistens my mouth. I cannot eat, but the hot sweet
tea eases my sphincters back to their customary laxity and
awareness, as I recall the French saying, "It tastes like
the good Lord in velvet pants sliding down your throat,"
the atheist's pathetic attempt to get on close terms with
the Host.

There are more cells in the basement, filled with junkies and Lesbians from the Village parties the cops keep crashing two or three times a month. Marie's rambling comments distract me from the choking, sobbing, moaning, and retching downstairs. Up here, the cheerleaders take over, screaming for more towels. The matron takes her time, snapping back: "So what? You won't bleed to death!"

That seething repartee takes me back to my fourteenth year's belief that the menstrual flow leaked from an ever-open wound that would not heal for more than thirty days at a time.

My ankles have stopped swelling. They still look forcefully pregnant. My feet hurt from their solitary all-night dance. One by one, we are taken out of our cells. Where are the Christians who will devour us? I put my hands over my ears while the matron shakes and pulls at the locks, and flings the whistling doors ajar.

Marie's face, close, shows nothing but petulance and greed for what is to come upon the others. Packed in the office room, we sit together on benches. Cops come and go briskly, counting us, yelling at one another to hurry up, for Mike's sake.

"What have we got this morning?" They call the roll. My husband's name is mispronounced and joked at, as usual, and for the first time it hurts. The sewer downstairs breaks loose and foams up to the surface. It seems our cells were a PTA meeting place, compared to what is pouring out of the basement. Every female staggering in adds its own shudders, shakes, yawns, belches, and farts, to the already booming cacophonic orchestration. Granma spits on the floor and tells off a cop, who takes it with a grin. Marie tries a few social graces and smoothes her dress. As we file through the door, I stare up at the dark glass pane into the hollow eyes of my son's mother. I will never forgive the slut. There is little mercy in me.

They take us through the porch into a closed van waiting in the sun. There is room for all of us to crouch tight with much hiccuping and sniffing. I focus on the three white girls from the downstairs cells.

Number One is a tall, disheveled, platinum-bleached youngster with translucent skin in a thin white crepe dress. Her neck, wrists, and earlobes dangle and throb with costume jewelry. She vomits quietly between her feet, taking great care to keep her beaded shoes out of the mess. She wipes them now and then with a piece of Kleenex extracted from her bra. Her hands are scratched raw and so is one of her legs, down to a thin ankle bracelet. Her dress is torn in the back. She wears on her quivering head the tiara of disorderly conduct, heavy with the mute disapproval of us all.

Number Two, an elaborately coiffured, skinny damsel, overly made up, sits on one buttock, holding close around her a worn black silk suit with pleated skirt. When she turns her other profile on me, I see, neatly drawn out on her powdered cheek, a huge fist mark with all the knuckles showing in dark blue. Her auburn hair is piled up high, her face frozen and taut. She keeps her feet turned in gauchely, and I see that the straps on her pumps are held together with scotch tape.

The sickest tomato in my corner, Number Three, is a well-rounded little blonde with short flat bangs and beauty marks. She sticks out her lower jaw and munches and crunches agonizingly, rocking her head left and right.

Her skirt rides up on chubby-smooth thighs, way up above her stocking tops. She tries to keep away from the vomit and manages it well enough between fits, but when the pain knifes her back, she stamps her feet in it, splashing everybody, then curses as soon as she finds her breath. And out again goes her gritting jaw. Marie tells her: "Don't you worry, honey, they'll give you some in court." But Honey, pulling at her Star of David, as if the chain was strangling her, does not hear a thing, turning all the consciousness she has left into anger against the tall fetid girl who did not know when to stop guzzling and raising hell.

I am turning into a thing once more: I have a weight, a shape, a color, a smell. I become a part of Marie's grin, of Honey's thighs, of Granma's jelly bosom, of Frozen Face's fist mark, of Rosa's blue wormy leg veins, of those dangling shoelaces on Sue's shoes. They are men's shoes.

The van stops. It seems the cops believe in letting the boys join us. In climb half a dozen young hoods, hand-cuffed two by two. Each has to lift up the other one's hand to be able to scratch his own head or crotch. They look far away from it all, and Honey watches them with jealous eyes, between two spasms. Sneakers slipping in the vomit, they cling to one another, in a moving bunch that twice falls over our lap. They scramble up to their feet, handcuffs clicking, without a word, as we go on staring at the perforated holes in the back of the van, through which we can see cars go by and traffic lights change from red to green.

It does not seem credible, but by now I am used to the corny taste of my Maker, and I do not hesitate to recognize young Fred Cooper, one of my favorite Johns (not

166

much of a talker), driving leisurely to his office, in his silver-gray Lincoln, which isn't paid for yet. Like most of the drivers, he looks at the van, then turns his eyes away. He follows us for a while, his manicured hands light on the wheel, his collar pin straight, then leaves us behind, on Third Avenue, so ending his brief encounter with our load of unwashed flesh.

Thinking of Fred, I mean Coops, is refreshing, and I let that Lincoln take me for a ride. Coops spent a night in my place last month. He was my first evening job, coming at six o'clock direct from a cocktail party where he downed a dozen martinis just because his wife was trying to stop him. Once in my bed, with a creamy hard-on, he fell asleep like a baby, choked up in his gold chain like Honey now. I pulled at it, letting the medals nest in the curly black hair of his chest, covered him with a sheet, and wrote the following note: "Fred, you drunken pig, I do not have the heart to kick you out, so go ahead and sleep."

I put the note down on his pants which I had to pick up and fold. Then I got dressed and hair-sprayed and went out for the night shift: Bradley, at Carnegie House, stewed too, sweet Ronnie Kent on Sixty-fourth Street—he pleaded to keep me all night, as usual—and the last, but most trying one, Rear-lover Manfred, whose little girl went to school with my son two years ago.

Home at two o'clock, I had to push Coops against the wall to get in bed. Tired as I was, I still took my make-up off so that he would not think, when waking up, that I looked exactly like his wife the morning after.

Early next day, he made leisurely, violent love to me. Doing all the work himself, as a man should. Pulling my head away, laughingly, as I kneeled down to kiss him. Turning me around and pushing me up and dragging me on the side of the bed and folding my legs up and bending me over, making me feel inside, all that time, the shaking, bouncing, throbbing, swelling, demential friction of his member, that held me transfixed and moaning, for all the time he decided I needed more.

In so much discomfort and anguish, the thought of orgasm washes over me like a purifying wave, mocking my Maker who did not expect to prove his point that way, and, at the same time, filling my loins with longing, as I crush my thighs together and call myself names for feeling horny at a time like this.

In the court building, a smelly elevator takes us up to the proper floor, after we have been parted from the boys. There, from room to room, files are made out on each of us, we are stripped and searched by matrons, kept sitting on benches, standing in halls, counted two by two, called in by batches of five, sent back all together, and our names are yelled at us again.

I remember saying that I had no family left to be notified in case of accident. I remember sticking a lit cigarette in Rosa's lips just to shut her up. I remember sitting in a room with a couple of tar-black twin sisters in jeans, busy taking care of each other's shakes, both stretched out on the side, their stomachs panting. They wipe the sweat from each other's faces. They tell me they got arrested in a newly opened cat house that did not pay the police quite enough. They will get a fix from the doctor so that they can stand up in front of the judge and answer: "Yes, your Honor." I thought I was flat-chested! Those girls have nothing at all, not one pennyworth of breast meat. I feel for them. What a show they must have to put on to make up for that choirboy handicap. . . .

In the next room to which I am herded, I see that Honey got her medicine. She sleeps, curled on the bench, her mouth half-open, her eyelashes still wet. Frozen-Face, in a fiery voice, is raving against some bartender who set her up. Half a dozen girls listen to her, all ready to follow with their own bartender stories. I reflect I would not have any. The closest I get to a bar, professionally, is when I meet kind white-haired Mr. Maurice who owns The Creole Crib and treats me to a drink or two before he takes me to his office couch. He uses his restaurant's napkins for towels. I like to think that, after laundering, they reappear close to his patrons' soup plates.

Those are the serious-minded prosts who do not mix junk with whoring. They stay with the doctor and his nurse only long enough to have their mouths examined for ulcers, their blood tested, and their insides smeared. It is my turn. I cannot fail to notice that the old doctor's face is covered with an ugly rash. (Handling radium goes with getting a few burns.) He gives me a fatherly pat on the behind and a shot of just-in-case penicillin. The nurse says, meaning it: "I don't want to see you again." I go back to our current waiting room, now as reeking hot as a stable.

We are handed containers of sweetened chicory and rancid bologna sandwiches. As I throw the bread and meat in a wastebasket, my eyes meet with a tall, slim, fawnlike Negro whom I will call Beauty from now on, even though her nose is broken by a slight bump. Her tight quivering nostrils, her fresh fruity mouth pushed forward faintly, her gleaming even teeth, the radiance of her cappuccino skin, mark her with the stamp of royalty.

Her hair is very short and woolly, with some lost attempt at straightening. Her legs seem to eat up the willing three-quarters of her body. They are long-stem and suavely rounded in an elongated way, just short of emaciation. A few muscles stir here and there, suggesting impatience and mobility kept in restraint but soon to be released. Hers must be the tiniest bones for not showing through that spare frame where you do not know what rules, toughness or fragility.

She half sits against the wall, her skirt pushed up to her crotch. She yawns, pointing one hip, then the other, her ankles askew, shrugging one lifted shoulder, tilting her long regal neck. There is no pretense, no self-consciousness, no complacency, no search for effect in her poise and coordination. Every time she moves, she breaks something in me, then creates another perfection of gesture which I swear cannot be surpassed till she destroys it with one better. She tops her own score by the minute. Nobody seems to notice her and I can see nobody else. Nobody sees me fall in love.

What Dior or Balenciaga would pay for her, I have no idea. But they could not spoil her if they tried, they could not tame her into giving up her guts, her right to be lazy, sloppy, and unwashed when she feels like it. One look at her and you know that nothing was forced upon her. All her choices have been made freely. At the same time, I wish I knew a way to shame the world into facing that, all over Harlem, every day she is not getting pushed around in jail, the crownless queen, the fairest of all, prances and glides by smelly street corners, surrounded by an improbable aura of black angel's hairs and undiscovered gems, that would prove, if they were to materialize, resolutely unworthy of her glory.

I feel, with sure sadness, that I will not be able to speak to her. How can you make small talk with Divinity? Spellbound, tongue-tied, I just stare at her, enraptured by a vision of what her heart must look like: a thickly cobwebbed diamond egg. I continue my patient, ferocious autopsy, unsatisfied with what my eyes can see. Any minute now, she might answer my mad command by turning inside out and show, to me only, the lining of fuming visceral splendors she is hiding.

While I am gladly losing my mind over her, from inside those walls where she will stay cornered all her life, she is talking to old Rosa. They share cigarette butts, and as she crushes the last one to the floor with a kick of her left spiked heel, I hear my princess explain, in a smooth sandpapered voice, to her faraway friend, how "the man" nabbed her on a roof, uptown, last night, after she had been staying home for two weeks, good and lazy, busy with what she likes best: "doin' nothin'."

"But my own man didn't have no more dough. And this bum on Lenox was after my ass for two bucks, and I seen them two guys in the car but I think to myself I can always get out from the back. I know the roofs up there better'n my own cunt. I shouldn't have went up that partic'lar one 'cause they got it all smashed and messy since they had that stabbin' last month. Got all excited 'bout one little knifin', they did, all of a sudden, don't ask me why. And my trick is actin' mean, and I says to myself: 'Shit, Lucy, you're done.'"

The language she uses grieves me only because I know she knows no other. I play at speaking like this, and thinking like this, as I play at being a whore. But you can tell Beauty has never been and never will be anything else, which makes me more of a phony than she is.

Right now, she uses the right words, if not the right syntax, for the things she is talking about. After all, between a trick and her own man, proper English does not come up with any fitting description. But her "slanguage" will. Let the articulate former art teacher with lots of tricks and no man of her own tell you so.

The probation officer must have called her name, for she rises. She does not just get up, but, like a snake lifted by sheer inner power, she elevates herself in all gathered strength and meekness. Her whole body is ravished away by the Dance, without any buttocks-wriggling. Not that they keep still, those joyous sprightly cheeks, deeply slit in their middle like an Irish cop's chin, but they are well above looking sexy: they *are* sex, its storm, its rainbow. Then she has a way of putting all of her weight on one leg—hem tight half across her thigh—and letting the other leg slide up forward, toes pointed, that hits you like two thousand violins holding together the highest note.

Aimée Kovacs, Rosa Gonzales, and Sue Wilson are summoned to the court. I drag myself up. I do not rise. Pushed across a number of halls with a number of girls, then up two flights of stairs, I find myself in the back room of one of the courts.

Girls are sitting or standing with the cops who arrested them and the legal advisers the City provides for those who do not have a private lawyer, as is the case with most. Here is the money-paved narrow way between the streetwalker or B. girl with a few bucks and cents (if any) up her stocking top—the bills folded, the coins stuck with a piece of adhesive tape—and the call girl with a bank account.

Here is another tip to remind me that call girls, though they belong in criminal courts like any other hustler, are usually not found there, unless they have been exceptionally unlucky or exceptionally framed. I will ponder over both technicalities as soon as I am out of here.

The girls are bumming cigarettes from the cops. The cops are showing the girls, not without a degree of exasperation and rough fondness, that they were real dopes to let themselves be caught again, and that, when they get out, they'd better not go back to the same street corner or barstool, for Pete's sake. Legal advisers are pushing everybody and his sister to plead guilty, even those who "never saw no money an' got picked up before they picked up nobody." Sue, who shares a chair with me, points to a young fellow with rabbit ears as one of the team that picked up Lucy Robinson. It takes me a while to realize that such is the name Beauty disguises herself with. I look at this shame of the species. He does have a normal face and wears clothing of man-made material. He is followed by my blond cop who waves at me and yells: "Here you are."

Beauty's knave looks around: "Mine isn't here yet. Not that I'd mind if she came up after everybody'd left."

He laughs delightedly, keeping his eyes up and down and around the only white female in the room: me. Though white I am not sure I still am, with dirt integrating my skin all over. He asks reproachfully, staring at my medals: "Irish?" I do not answer and my cop says: "Temper."

Every ten minutes or so, a tearful girl rushes out of the

courtroom, escorted by cops who try to keep her wailing comments to a minimum. Old Rosa's soft-shoe number is greeted by winks, nods, and some discreet applause. She is taken away, protesting that she never went with no man. For one thing she can't stand them. She then resorts to Spanish to give her opinion of the judge.

One happy face, Granma's, makes me bloom with relief: the judge was easy on her, and let her off with a warning. She must have reminded him of his own mother. She repeats that she won't be hangin' around no more. Her only trouble is keepin' fellows away from her, but she sure won't do the chasin' no more.

The twins follow shortly. They smile at me, passing by. They will be together in the House of *Delectation,* for three months. Plenty of time to rehearse their act in the sick ward. From one house to the other. It makes a lot of sense. With the merciful dose of Eden the doctor shot into them an hour ago, they will not know the House of D. from their elbow tonight. Tomorrow will be another story. Tomorrow will be history.

My big cop, Saul, is waving at me from the courtroom door. I enter the sanctuary of Law. I am led to a bench— one more—in front of the judge. Enzo, close to me, behind a littered desk, looks green in the face. Is it the light or his liver? I suddenly feel detached and cheerful. I grin at him, completely out of context. He does not reciprocate with the kind of look a man bestows on a wondrous wench, arrested for obscenity or not. I am starting to see the fun of it all, and, right there and then, after a whole night of doleful dissolving in grief and penance, I decide to face my nemesis. Thank you, Beauty.

It is not the proper time to advertise my new mood,

174

and I lower two sorrowful eyes, keeping my body erect and my shoulders unswerving. I hear Enzo Crezzione ask for bail, which the judge puts up pretty high: two hundred dollars. The case is postponed. My lawyer then presents the court with his intention of pleading not guilty. He underlines that we are dealing with a first offense of a "particular character." It has been particular for centuries. The court grudgingly takes note, and I am led out, after learning through Enzo's bad breath—so it *is* his liver—that I will be free in a few hours.

I have been told that I will see the light tonight, but I decide to prepare myself for the eventuality of staying at the House of D.—the House of Daniels. What are we girls doing in the court building, now that all has been said and done? We count each other and find out that everybody got postponed or sentenced, but that nobody is getting out except old Anna. I will be the only one out on bail, if all goes well. It is obvious that everybody else's "own man" keeps to himself the few bucks left over from yesterday's tricks, if any.

I do not see Beauty. I hear she was the last one in court. We leave the building for our last grand carriage of that very eventful day, before she joins us. As the outside doors are closing behind us like a mouth that cannot wait to spew us out, I see her, the apple of my eye, followed by a horsy matron, trot up to the van on her winged ankles, her face sullen and fierce, her eyes bloodshot, and I know the judge has been blind. May the earth swallow him.

This is a peaceful ride for the girls, with none of the tension of this morning. They surrender to a higher command of submission and misery. For many of them the worst happened, and they are used to the worst. Aloud, they worry for their men, left alone, who will be more demanding when they come out. The Law struck, and they expected to get hit, but they resent being kept waiting for the blows to fall: and that unnecessarily dragged-out day sickens them more than the actual sentence it brought down on them.

Quite a few have done time already in the House. All know about it in detail. When I was living in its neighborhood, I was asked to sign a petition against its maintenance. I heard all the talk about its crowded and dirty cells, the toughness of its hacks who are supposed to enjoy their jobs no end and to pursue no love affair with the Board of Health. The food is said to have bugs in its starch, and you get slapped around for looking fit. My masochistic impulses are left untickled. I might use those images in some future fantasy, but it is as far as I wish to go. When I want my face slapped for kicks, for bread, or for both, I am big enough to call the right number and set my hair in advance. I am aware of the fact that you do not get slapped for kicks in the House of Delectation, and you are definitely kept from making bread. As for kicks and bread together, the Law clearly does not believe in dishing it out to the transgressors, judged and sentenced as they are by magistrates who do all right for themselves in both departments.

I fear for Beauty. She broods, her brow set in a hard line, her chin jutted out, her nose pinched. When she speaks, it is at the peak of her fever, her breasts sharp and trembling, her belly taut, with the navel sucked in, as she bangs her closed fist on her knees. It seems that she will, with serenity, get slapped, eat bugs broiled or fried, sleep in a smelly cot with somebody's feet on her stomach. What she cannot take is: number one, that dirty cop who put his hand on her left tit, right before she went to the judge; number two, what that mother-humper told her about her own man being picked up this afternoon. Follows a long frantic story about what her man did *not* do, last month, and with whom. I stop paying attention to her words to let my eyes drink her in and plug her good-by.

She does not succeed in lifting the girls out of their apathy. Quite a few do not listen. I wish Marie was there. On Marie's thick, crusty humor and curiosity, Beauty's anger would not bounce back, but sink in and lighten. Marie must be preceding us in one of the other vans, unless grand larceny deserves another home than the House of D., a distinction she would be, I know, most appreciative of.

What could I tell Beauty? She has heard, I am sure, that I am not going to stay in the House. News travels fast. I remember Ossie telling me that, in the pen, inmates would know, well in advance, when a new batch of prisoners was due, how many faggots there would be among them, and what their names were, so that they started, even before laying eyes on them, to plan, bet, and fight over every one of those much expected bedfellows.

But, oh wonder, Beauty is now looking at me. She asks, all her fury deflated, if I know Marsilly, close to Paris. Her man had been there, a long time ago. He even knocked up a girl in a bakery shop. I nod my head, in unadulterated geographic defeat, unable to lie under

177

Beauty's severe stare, and I see her turn away, disbelieving plainly that I am French at all, or that I had ever set foot in that country.

We are getting close. Pressing my forehead against the back of the van, I can see the gate of the House, the dirty brick walls. We stop. A few men at work on the sidewalk lean on their shovels, grinning and waving at the van. When they see our soiled flock of black sheep file defiantly in front of them, they stop the welcoming cheers, which shows they have better taste than the wisecracking cops who take us in.

The tank of the House is in all points similar to the hall of a big school, all the way down to that undisputed fact: children do not willingly enter the Castle of Learning. They are sent by their elders. The same prevailing solicitude enrolls us here against our will: we would rather play outside.

Sitting at the desks, busy behind the booths, pushing us around the benches like traffic cops, are the famous colored guards, most of them formidable Walkyries, more butchy-looking than the manliest Village amazons. It is my first contact with them. I marvel at how well fitted those broads are to the job. It is a pleasure to see such talents unwasted.

They are informed right away by the cop who led us in, that, among the three last vanfuls of prisoners, one, only one, and white at that, will not be staying, and you can see they are not overly pleased. The house is full, but their hospitality boundless. They will not be speedy about taking care of my papers. It is a good thing too: I want to watch. I sit down at a desk, while the other girls, after being parted once more from their belongings, are confined to the benches; I dare not look at them.

A hand on my shoulder. A bright green sleeve. A whiff of bitter, hairy sweat. It is Marie, minus the bouffant sleek wig, which they just took away from her. Marie, with a face as small as a clenched fist and the eyes of a sad monkey who will try a few somersaults, even after the mood for jumping is gone. She purses her lips, and as a hack grips her arm, she yells: "Good luck, Frenchie."

I have just the time to plead with her: "Take care of Beauty."

I see her mouth a mute "Who?" as she is led away to the farthest bench. I failed. Beauty does not exist, and Lucy Robinson is going to be very much alone.

Marie, who greeted me as I was being searched and bade me farewell at the time of my release, Beauty, who moved me to love and left me with the remorse of not tending to this love, Old Rosa, unaptly wrapped in your scorched skin—for how much longer? Honey, dead still in your sleep, Frozen-Face with the bartender-bruised cheek, Sue in the men's shoes, tongue-sticking Bess, now dreading the sting of fresh iodine on your arm, I am leaving you, and it is not fair.

I am taken to a hall which looks onto the street. My first steps are cautious. I fight the urge to look over my shoulder. Cannot help waiting for the others. I look up into Cass's worried face. I throw my arms around his warm neck, then remembering how much I stink I let him go sign the bail's receipt. I walk across to kiss Ossie's cheek, which reminds me of something out of the Gospel, upside down. I shake Enzo's hand, repeating a few inane

179

things about how bright the sun is. We walk out on the sidewalk, Cass catching up with us. Enzo tells me to go sleep it off.

I climb in a cab with Ossie, Cass following us on his scooter. I wonder where Marsilly is. I see Beauty's man, hiding in the baker's oven, his breath short, his fly bulging, soon humping on a pile of flour-bags, then getting up almost as white as the girl who lies there, pleased and ashamed, every other night. Marsilly. . . . It is Ossie's turn to drop Kents in my lap. I say: "I smoked a Pall Mall yesterday." Ossie talks about more payoff for the cops. They want three hundred each. It will be my job to reach Paul Flint and make sure of his intentions.

I ask Ossie to stop the cab. I must buy sanitary napkins. I see Cass's scooter shoot past us. Walking out of the drugstore, mentally counting my change, I give my love to the brown paper bag I am holding and to the sunny spots my feet step around reverently. They are mine to trespass in and out of, and I hopscotch my way among them, Ossie blinking at me. Out of jails, people wrap things for you and let you out on sun-striped sidewalks.

As soon as the three of us musketeers are at the studio, the phone rings. It is Saul the cop calling from across the street. So there were four of us on our way from the House, after all. Cass opens his wallet. Ossie extends his paw and makes for the stairs. Cass and I both watch him from the window as he hands an unusual pack of cigarettes to an invisible applicant, hidden behind the parking lot phone both. Cass had only sixty dollars on him. That means there will be more payments to make, if I go along with the scene. Ossie climbs back up. I feel some tension between my friends. The Mutt looks denser by the minute, shoulders hunched, back turned meatily on the Snake who soon leaves, very straight, after reminding me that he cannot let me stay in his apartment: he has a tenant there, but that I am welcome in Kismet, Fire Island, the gang's weekend place, anytime I want, before and after my day of reckoning at court. He gives me his key to the beach house.

I close myself in the bathroom and lustily indulge in a disappearing trick that involves half a bar of soap. I realize, with doting humility, how close I have lived to my body's juices these past two days, as I watched neglect creep on, hour after hour, and take charge of every pore, shock discolor my face and chisel it right down to the bones, fear soak through my skin under its dirt and dried blood.

I wash my clothes, stiff with filth and perspiration, and change into an old pair of slacks that I left here last month. Ossie gives me his only clean T-shirt, that rubs my brassiere-free nipples to sweet unpadded life. He fills a tall glass with ice cubes and water, makes me lie on the couch with my feet up. Wending their painful way up my crotch, blue veins bulge on my ankles, putting me in a good place as a future competitor for Old Rosa's title.

All around is the customary disorder of coiled film reels, files, and bills cushioning every seat. A camera stands on a tripod, facing a table where three dozen loaves of rye bread are set in a pyramid: yesterday's shooting. Props pile high, discarded in a hurry. Sheets of white paper are draped on the floor and hung from the walls, ripped in places. What should appear busy and lived-in merely spells out sloth and abandon. Only Ossie's darkroom speaks for the respect of a craft that can be conduced with neatness. He cleaned the would-be living room cubicle by sweeping Sims's and Nat's mess away from the couch and table. He finds a pillow for me and gives me a light with a choleric sigh that deflates my own lungs.

After letting Ossie ventilate, from us both, assorted pangs of relief and sorrow, in that long single eruption of breath, we resume the need for self-mockery that bound us together and give in to it in an uncontrollable nervous giggle. He thinks that I do not know what he is laughing at, but I will save all my surprises, just as I will let him save up all his juice, from now to St. Peter's day.

Ossie asks how it tastes to be free. I answer I feel no pain, but it may be all temporary. He tells me the studio is all ours tonight, if I do not mind the heat, and that I should move out of my apartment, in case the cops, regretful as they are of a wasted opportunity, feel like paying me a gallant visit. Some of my Johns also might come and ring my doorbell, unannounced, just to see what is going on, and my two guardian angels have insisted that I must have no gentlemen callers, since the house is officially under watch. They added that I could have all the business I wanted outside. Do they want to make sure I keep hitting the town, using that fine money-green comb they look forward to to clean of a few more goldilocks?

Ossie tells me of his fight with Cass, who does not think it advisable to deal with the cops any further, criticizes Enzo's approach to the case, and judges that the whole thing has been played wrong from the start, "with a touch of hoodlumism." Ossie knocks himself on the head a few times at the remembrance of that crack, made in a noncommittal Wall Street forecasting way, about "wolves in sheepskin," and I beg him not to get excited because I am on the verge of a headache.

Furious to see that I will not take sides, Ossie turns to the phone, orders two malted milks downstairs, fishes one dusty aspirin tablet out of Nat's ashtray, among shirt-buttons, pieces of chalk, rolled prophylactics, safetypins and rubber bands.

We go for a drive in sister Silvana's car, which should have taken us yesterday to eat those ill-fated jinx-burgers I will never taste.

The car top is down. I am free. My skin smells of soap. I am free. Ossie's beard is scratchy. He retrieves his right arm from around my shoulders, then puts it back again. My neck easily cuddles inside and out of his armpit, anticipating the traffic command. I am free.

He tells me: "You don't know what life is like unless you've gotten out of jail at least once." I do not try to deny it. New York's night is a gift fostered on me only, and I feel far from ungrateful.

We pick up Silvana in the Bronx. Who but Ossie would have as a favorite sister an accident-prone, explosive, curly divorcee, as earthy as a kitchen table, unpredictable in the ways of a plane's jammed propeller, full of sober fun and bizarre insight.

She recalls for a while the tribulations she went through to raise three hundred dollars that got Ossie—whom she insists on calling Junior—out on bail, one rainy night four winters ago. Her dog happened to be sick, and she took it with her, craftily, from neighbor's door to door, pleading with old schoolfriends, her own mother and relatives, the grocery's customers, bartenders, her arms wrapped around twelve pounds of feverish shaggy black poodle. As she surmised it, Frisco's drooling mouth and throbbing belly served her brother's cause, that night, to the point that, feeling sorry for her sick pet, the whole neighborhood, not out of any fondness for Ossie, parted with six hundred's worth of Anglo-Saxon mistiness. All of them adding the following comment: "And for the love of God, take that poor dog *back home* this minute."

We ride around as I give them a light account of my most pregnant memories of the day. I do not mention Beauty, for what is there to say? I can hear Ossie ask what is so special about a skinny nigger. I stare at the cigarette butts in the ashtray, thinking how the girls would fight for them. Silvana, tossing fistfuls of curls away from her hostile face, drips at me such liquid looks of anxiety that I try to shake up my drugged state of well-being. I thought I had a right to relax tonight without somebody's sister silently begging me to watch out.

I must pick up a few things at home. Ossie parks on the corner of Lexington and Twenty-fifth. I climb the stairs, feeling like a visitor. In the kitchen, I almost topple over the chopping block and its load of green candles stuck in the necks of champagne bottles. Ossie catches my arm in time and sighs: "You'll die from bumps and knocks before long, in your own place, like a real homebody you should have been."

The smell of my home leaps at me, attacking me from all sides, as I recall with every sultry whiff that I must soon leave it behind. It takes a body some time to achieve that noseful of a melting pot around bed, writing table, kitchen closet, linen drawers. I had hardly three months to work on it, and I concocted a pretty unexampled blend of sour and sweet and spicy. You can part from a place with a straight face; not so from a smell that does not play fair.

I point to the dirty glasses in the sink: I ask nastily: "You in a breaking mood, Ossie?" He winces so hard that Silvana says "Touché." She does not know what I am referring to, but she knows her brother's face. She reads it like a defenseless paperback.

Between me and that empty gin bottle lies a short stretch of unsavory time I wish I could make wisdom with. The bed gapes, just as Paul left it. I strip the sheets from the mattress, kicking them in a corner with the towels, Ossie and Silvana watching me. The photograph books are still open on the rug. I snap them shut and put them away. I throw a dress, a sweater, some undies, a pair of pajamas, toiletries, and my toothbrush in a small suitcase, still looking around for all the things the cops touched and misplaced yesterday.

Suddenly, I see, profiled in its void-filled corner, under the telephone stand, I see what is missing: my camera, Daniel's gift. I remember how they took it out of its case, asked questions about it, pointed it at me, as if it was full of bullets, meaning to be funny.

"They must have come back for it after I'd left, sweet. No problems with locks when you have a badge."

That is Ossie's comment to my wail of loss. I treasured that camera. I can still see Daniel's beaming face when I took my first photograph, upside down. I was starting to get the feel of it. I planned to take it with me to France and shoot my son, all summer. The cops may have come back to steal it, as Ossie is so ready to suggest. I have only a thief's word for it. Once a whore, always a whore.

I tell Ossie to take the TV set. He can watch the bang-bang movies he likes in the studio, when I am gone. If I am free to go. I hope Daniel remembers his promise about letting me use one of his warehouses to store my furniture. We shall see what Daniel remembers. I wish I could keep this place just as it is: tacky hallways, nosey janitor, high old-fashioned ceilings, antique kitchen stove and fixtures, kidney-shaped tub, cats and dogs in the backyard and all the friendly pigeons. But both the police and my landlady see things differently.

Next year, I will have to tame another set of rooms and curb my horror for change, my distrust of new wallpaper and doorknobs, in another just-bought ill-fitting garment of unknown walls.

Ossie, untroubled, goes down with the TV set. I follow, carrying my suitcase. Silvana closes the door, cursing softly at the world.

There will be no place of my own to come back to, after my summer stay in France, and its stretch of relatives' homes to shelter me and the boy. This is the Professor's condition: that I should stay within constant family bounds, for as long as the child is with me, "so that our son will not risk being contaminated" by my un-diluted contact. I quote.

In the car, I suggest breathily: "I guess I'll get Daniel to buy me another camera." Ossie brightens up: "That's the idea, sweet," with the quickness of approval of the rehearsed bit. Silvana drops us at the studio. She hugs me: "I don't have to tell you to sleep good, honey, I know you will."

The studio is one beautiful scorcher. I cannot wait to

lie down. "What day is today, Ossie?" He laughs. "Tuesday night, sweet. I know, just one day in the can, and the calendar is back-assed."

The cops may have come back. And they may not. It could have been Ossie's share, for a start. A deal? Fear sides with shame, turning my doubts to guilt. I cannot afford to lose faith in Ossie. Not right now. Until proved innocent. . . . So there is a court of justice in my heart.

It takes me a few minutes to fall asleep, sweating on a cool sheet, while Ossie is still messing around the darkroom. He spent the afternoon in court and must now finish Nat's work, as usual. Last night he ran all over the Bronx, in search of a lawyer; and here I am, accusing him of playing God knows what patient con game.

Beauty, where are you? What did you eat tonight? What did they give you to wear? As I was waiting for my bail papers, I saw a few inmates go up and down the stairs, clad in gray hospital gowns with letters and numbers printed in the back. I fall asleep, picking numbers for you.

12

May 25th

Next morning, Ossie takes me back to Twenty-sixth Street, where I write checks for Enzo, Cass, and my landlady, while he cuts the wire on my doorbell and calls the phone company to have my number disconnected at once. Then we part after an uneasy hug. I go to the bank to get some cash and I call Daniel. I meet him in his car half an hour later. He promises to send a truck and two men to move my things out to his warehouse. Crushed by the news of my arrest and pending trial, he has just enough guts to can his "I told you so," but not enough to make good last week's offer to take me on his boat this coming weekend.

"The police may be following you, chérie, please don't think I am afraid for myself."

I darkly intimate that I am not going to spend this weekend alone. I jump out of the car, leaving Daniel to his misery.

I settle down in a phone booth and call my answering service. Twelve Johns left messages. I will not check with them. It is too soon yet to trust myself to speak to a John.

I have not cooled off. Daniel is different: I need his help. He told me once too often that I could count on him, no matter what.

I call Sheil to beg her to be careful. I have that feeling that it will be her turn next. She knows what happened, through Cass, and she has a dozen excited questions. I have no energy to answer. I cut her short, intending to start packing at home. Tomorrow I will work at reaching Paul Flint. I will see my landlady and let her know that she is going to have a clean house again. I call Ossie and brief him about the scene with Daniel. He laughs: "Don't take it out on him."

It is Ossie's boy-scout night tonight. Once every other Tuesday, he plays father to a gang of kids in his parish, his own two sons being among the group. He spends most of his weekends taking them for hikes in the country, on his time.

Ossie's boy-scout night helps with the fuzz, too. When they pick him up for questioning, cops are impressed by Father O'Keenan's warm recommendation scribbled on the back of St. Anthony's image. Father O'Keenan received Ossie's confession, last year: "You must try to give back the money you stole, my son."

"Forget it, dad, I mean Father. I don't even remember half of the joints. . . . You see, Father, let's say you blow a safe—my schtick was drugstores, remember, 'cause of all those juicy drugs around. Well, as I said, when you bust a drugstore, man, half the time you don't even know where the damn. . . ."

"Shadduck, that will do!"

Maybe Father O'Keenan was not entirely fooled by

Ossie's never missing Sunday Mass, but he knew when a stud needed a break, and he made it easy for Ossie to apply and succeed as a "father of the week" within the parish limits. I had never seen him with kids, but I knew he had what it takes: no condescension, serene ingenuity, and the patience of the weak.

At home, the silence of the phone makes me cringe. Suddenly I am too tired to do much of anything. I lie on my bed, wondering about my clientele and trying to make plans for the weekend since Daniel is chickening out. I whip my buttocks lightly with the tip of the dogwhip and pile up all the others on my bed: the cat-o'-nine-tails, neatly braided, the leather paddle, the stiff bamboo crop, the steel-centered black crop, thin as a blade, with a red silk tip made to tickle the restrained object of delectation, the bleached horse-hair whip, soft as the drunk Lesbian's hair. Jim gave them all to me. Each has its story. Maybe I should spend the weekend with my master, if he will have me.

I cannot go to Kismet yet and face Cass's questions about Ossie. I fall asleep, after putting under my pillow the letter I received this morning from Michel. For Mother's Day: a big heart filled in with yellow pencil and three words of love. Gone to waste.

May 29th

Thursday and Friday, I let panic take over. I cannot reach Ossie on the phone for a long time and when I do he sounds vague, irritable, and horribly thick-voiced. I go see Ruggieri Kormann in the pearl-gray suite of the Jansen building where, last year, I waited around for his friends to drop in and take me to some hotel room, bachelor flat, or one of those office back rooms where I hooked my garter belt between the safe and the swivel chair.

Ruggieri Kormann has not heard a word from Paul Flint and throws his arms in the air at the mention of my predicament. He gives a few embarrassed phone calls in French, Italian, and Yiddish, to try and reach the people through whom he met Paul. It seems now he never knew him too well. He saw him twice at parties; they exchanged a couple of dirty jokes. Paul looked like a "regular guy." All Ruggieri gets on the phone now is a bunch of excuses. Maybe Paul spread the word already that he was not to be put in contact with me. Ruggieri rolls his eyes around, says he is sorry and will try again tomorrow, while I am having a fit. Only Ossie can reach the cops to get them to start working on Paul. They are being paid for that after all. But I cannot even get Ossie to listen to me.

I have done most of my packing. Paintings and drawings are tied together, books and records, pots and pans piled in cardboard boxes, clothes folded in suitcases and bags, drapes and rugs gone to storage. I sleep in a wasteland, between stripped walls, in the middle of a deserted stage. Show is over. Time to move on.

Cass is polite with me. Sheil busy with our clientele. I find two messages from Jim at my service. I call him from an upstairs phone booth, in a luncheonette close to a noisy kitchen, where young Puerto Ricans with swelling crotches officiate and watch me plead, cry, and kick around, while I tell Jim how I have been killing time those last days. I melt at his kind words: "You won't be alone this weekend, Lily darling." I will meet him in Philadelphia, Saturday. "Be a good girl till then."

I will see Jim. I cling to that thought. He will whip me just enough so that I can relent. I will sleep all tangled up in him. A little of his warmth will rub off on me. It's head and tails between us, we flip the coin without kidding each other. I need his high hand over my defeats.

I am now parting with delusion number one: Ossie *is* back on dope. It leaves everything for me to fear. I have known it for some time but I refused to consider where it would lead. I imagine all kinds of schemes he may have pursued through me from the start. I remember the first night he kept watch over my sleep, from a low chair, and gave me an account of my nightmares the next morning. I am now tempted to give his *delicatesse* another name. The devious double edge is running thin, and I do not know which side the light is going to hit. I do not want to see that light.

I miss my work. It is a humbling discovery. I miss my Johns, I miss the carousing, the madness of not knowing whom you are going to lay next. So it was Show S. O. Biz, all right, but it was growing on me and I feel useless now. I walk around my neighborhood, jittery and faint with colic, looking over my shoulder, avoiding uniforms, peeking at any gray or green car parked close, from broken-down phone booths to busy ones. I end up in a cheap theater where an old Western rocks me to sleep over a hot dog leaking with mustard.

Out in the mellow sticky night I warm up at the drunken propositions of a bum on the make. What kind of

193

a slut am I to find thrills in the lowest search? Out of the sewer, girl! I call the studio and leave my fourth message of the day for an absent Ossie, crouched in some uptown cellar, in a deadly seventh heaven I refuse to let him succumb to, even if all I have to protect him with is my pride.

A little later, I call Cass at Annette's place, and make a grand first appeal. Then I go back home quickly to wait for him downstairs. (My buzzer does not function any more.) To hell with the frigging landlady. I see familiar spotless white slacks and shirt light up the dark bluish street, and I join the technicolor end-of-the-picture slushy effect by running to welcome the dear bastard. Cool and distant composure is what I get. Up in my bedroom, Cass drops on the bed while I sit on my heels, where the rug used to be, listening to a grim lecture about irresponsible females who "play but do not want to pay." I am as aware as ever that he is the most beautiful piece of stallion flesh I ever laid my remembering eyes on. Those females he is talking about sometimes show a foolish trust, totally misplaced, in "shady characters with luminous plans." On his best venomous behavior, Cass sobers me up in a clinical, sterile way, but I resent his resentment.

I see Enzo on Friday. I wait almost an hour in his Fifth Avenue backyard office. I handle the brother first. Those guineas always work with the pack. Long-toothed Antonio tries to persuade me to leave the "whole thing" to him, and the shortest cut to his elder brother's status proves to be a lengthy discussion of European womanhood. Enzo at last enters and after I have briefed him, with my legs crossed, about my vain attempts to reach Paul Flint and my doubts concerning Ossie, he makes me slip down to more general matters and I find myself on my knees, by his desk, gratifying a disorderly lawyer in shirt-sleeves, with the hope of a diminished fee lurking in the back of my mind and materializing unpleasantly around my tonsils as an illustration of conjugal starvation, as he unnecessarily explains later.

Riding back home in a cab, I wonder if I have not given out a free sample just for the love of the law.

I go see my landlady the same night. "Mrs. Pummels, you told me last month that you were ready to make it easy for me to break my lease?"

There are embroidered napkins everywhere and holy pictures. Maddening. I go on: "I expect to get my deposit back. I will move out next week. I will tell you the exact day as soon as I can."

The tall, solemn old lady warned me twice about leading a quiet life and keeping my goings-on to a minimum. Since that veiled threat, I never entertained men at night and felt sure that she was not home in the afternoon, when I had most of my business. But the janitor must have kept her well-informed. She may have been the one who wrote to the police, but now she is so contrite and concerned over me that I decide I must look like my own shadow. "I am just fine, Mrs. Pummels, thank you." That look she gave me prompts me to spend a busy evening in the bathroom. I shave my legs, and scrub my feet with a pumice stone. I oil my body after a long hot bath, then a cool shower, followed by ten minutes of wading in a tubful of cold water, to take the weight and fatigue off my legs. I steam my complexion clean, massage my face and scalp, pluck my eyebrows, file and polish my nails and mix in my hair a panful of warm henna paste which

I keep on in bed all night, my head wrapped in a thick towel.

Next day I fly to Philadelphia. I spend a dismal but cozy weekend, the whipping kept to a low, caressing point. I lie in bed, naked, against the body I just rubbed with hot towels, making my touch more tender over every vulnerable spot. My master is shining, as ever, with power, success, and his wife's and children's love for him.

I tell him about Ossie, my bodyguard, Cousin Cass whom I am afraid to forfeit, and, most unsettling of all, the discovery I made, in cell number two at the Tombs, of my niche of deepest rejection, along with a dark delectation against which my good sense vainly rebels. We know the pace, the ways, and the guises of the inner beast that tries to swallow me. The beast that had Jim within striking range a few years ago, when he was slumped, dead drunk, at the wheel, driving his car, every night, at killing speed. Those were the days when he had not learned yet to flirt with self-destruction. Now he cheats, but I still play for keeps, and Jim knows the stakes well enough to greatly fear.

We have our Saturday dinner in a dim oyster bar; then we walk around the park, sitting on benches, kissing and stroking each other, forgetting blissfully that we have a hotel suite across the gardens, sharing the forbidden public park frenzy of lovers without a roof with a number of stealthy couples pussyfooting around the trees, targets for our wildest bets. As ever, we extend the limits of our game to a pitch of make-believe forced into reality.

Sunday afternoon, we leave the Wellington Hotel. Jim drives me to the airport, and on the way we plan to spend

196

a few days in Cape Cod, "if everything goes well in court." Jim's last words are to bid me to call him as soon as I am through with the law.

June 2nd

On Monday, I finally catch Ossie at the studio. He hands me my books back, and sleepily promises to call the cops and ask them to start working on Paul Flint.

I meet Daniel, who buys me lunch at The Drunken Mermaid on Third Avenue, and chauffeurs me to the travel agency where, a week ago, I started getting information about a scheduled flight. Then, in a department store ladies room, I tear my address and telephone books to pieces and flush them down in a most fitting toilet noise. Before I so disposed of my trade's diminutive ledgers, I took the trouble to copy eighteen steadies' names, and six contacts', in another brand-new little book.

On Wednesday, I move out of Twenty-sixth Street, Daniel's men taking all my worldly possessions away to his Staten Island warehouse. I keep only my clothes, five suitcases of them, bound for Poitiers. I have them dropped at Dave Bernheim's studio. Good Dave expands his hospitality much further and offers me board and room. I pack a bag for Kismet, where I intend to spend the three days I have left before the Law takes over. (Or will it?)

I call Ossie to tell him that I am leaving. He assures me that the cops will be meeting Paul Flint tomorrow. He sounds almost normal. He asks if it would be a help to have Silvana drive me to Kismet tomorrow. He adds that

I am likely to end up in Canada. But I do not let that faze me. I call Silv myself and we make a date. I have a plan.

I see Enzo to rehearse the defense bit. After going over all those legal jokes, we come to the main course: his fee. He declares suavely that I owe him four hundred dollars more than the check for two hundred he received from me last week. My face shows shock. Enzo has the poor grace to go down to three seventy-five, all the while leaning on me and breathing hard. I pick up my gloves, stand, and make a haughty exit. I will send him two hundred dollars after the case is closed.

I am horny. I need somebody. Let us look at those remaining numbers. I would like it to be Ben. He is young, friendly, Jewish-chubby, and gentle in his ways. He never preaches to me. I call his private line. I cut him short: "Been a mess, Ben."

"When can I see you, funnybones?"

"Right now. I leave tomorrow for a house on the beach. A tiny house, a big beach. No men around till Saturday. Tonight I will sleep on a boat. I want to go to bed with you now. And misery makes me all the hotter."

He laughs: "What time shall I come up and minister to you?"

"You can't come up to my place. I don't have a place anymore. Trouble, I told you."

"O.K. My company has a room at the Biltmore this week. I'll meet you in the lobby in forty-five minutes."

I go for a drink in the hotel bar with Ben. Last time I had gin it was with the cops. It works fast. I am lusting and start rocking on my stool. Ben watches my eyes turn

198

soft. He leads me to the elevator quickly, as if he was afraid I might spill my zest. He carries my oversized beach bag, which makes his black briefcase look out of place.

Before I can reach the bathroom, Ben has me in his arms. I step out of my shoes: the dear boy is five foot seven. He caresses my neck, my ears, my mouth, with the tip of his tongue. My nipples harden and swell to half-decent size, pushing against the tight lace of my bra. Everywhere Ben touches me, my skin crawls and tightens. I think of Beauty in the police van, her arms entwined above her proud head.

A sweet awareness nibbles at the moist flesh between my thighs, digging deeper and deeper at the widening walls of my hunger. I feast on anticipation, tasting so strong a desire that it brings me fulfillment in itself. Ben plays at leaving my panties on, his thumb stroking the wet clinging nylon crotch, till I can bear it no more and send the damn thing flying over his head.

Ben dumps me on the bed and takes me with his fingers, leading them all the way up to the mouth of the womb, moving them sideways, then in a circular, accel-erated motion, so that I feel my rectum invaded, possessed by the same relentless friction. I call Ben's name many times in a single breath, my body arched high, clinging to his touch, daring him to stop. He goes on till I am all spent.

He withdraws his hand and shows me the stream of my own seed, trickling down my thighs. I smile at it in a daze, my head on the side, while he stares at my clitoris, still hard and shiny as a rosebud. I welcome Ben in me with all the juicy gratitude he made me able to contain and after he is still and heavy on me, I turn his head to face me and my eyes thank him so plainly that he cannot help reciprocating aloud: "That was my pleasure. . . ." But his voice comes out all squeaky because his throat is crushed against my shoulder and we laugh.

I shall not douche. It is good to stay soiled and smelly-happy around Ben's fingerprints. I wear a Kotex inside my panties, and my powers of retention are such, once aroused, that I do not lose one creamy drop. There is a time to spill and a time to save.

I am late to meet Daniel at Luchow's. He benefits all evening, all night, from the quietude Ben left me with. I am still inhabited by a swaying thrust that follows, precedes, and prolongates the natural motions of my body as I lean forward and backward to take my glass to my lips and put it down, hold my cigarettes to Daniel's lighter, slowly cross my knees.

I drink three Pernods with water. I feel so at peace with my glands that I do not resent my escort's hurry in telling the waiter: "*My wife* will have a side order of winekraut."

Over a baked apple, Daniel presents me with the small gold star I asked for. I put it on my neck chain with my medals. It is about time for the Star of David to acknowledge services rendered to the male species of the adventurous-nosed and lustrously doe-eyed tribe. I love them all, except Daniel of course. They are so shrewd and obvious and willing to be petted.

I remind Daniel that he should send for my rugs, still in storage. I want them to be kept with my other things

200

in his warehouse. We plan a four-day trip, after the court-room's throw of the dice, to Montauk, East Hampton, and Shelter Island. I remind myself that I have no place to stay, except Kismet, and the Cape with Jim. I will share my time in equal slices. Daniel feeds me the best and he respects my silent moods.

Since I told him what I did with my business books, the simpleton is in heaven and I let him get high hopes and relaxed purse-strings. I drink just enough to lose touch with the night chores to come: Daniel's double-bubble has been severely unattended lately, and he looks lecherous, which does not fit his pants' size. Better be dead, or fixed like a city cat, than have to beg for lust or buy it.

On the way to City Island pier, I fall asleep in Daniel's Cadillac, with a new camera cradled in my arms. I wake up in front of two rows of boats, twinkling and rocking atop the dark oily waters. I set foot on "Liza II," my home for the night. I can put my beach bag down now, in a doll's bedroom complete to the Paris street scenes. Daniel takes me around the boat, kept clinic clean by the captain. I admire the mahogany woodwork, the stuffed fish, and tiny kitchen, and after I have bungled my home-work in Daniel's bed, and managed to keep all that German food down, I crawl back to my own bed, still under the spell of those afternoon fingers whose lasting mel-lowed bruises have been left undisturbed by that rubber joke of a weak rabbit I just turned my derrière on.

I pretend to be asleep and do not answer his last try at probing my feelings by stating his own, once more. I am vaguely appalled by the fierceness of my hate for

201

Daniel. It is quite clear that he does not deserve it. I find a sharp pleasure in fooling him right down to the bone. Good night, Beauty, we had a blessed time this afternoon.

June 5th

On the way to Bay Shore, I am kept in stitches by the odyssey we make, Silvana and I, to find the right highway and leave it in time to reach our destination, so freeing the morning drivers of Silvana's beastly handling of the brakes.

This girl conceives speech as an exercise meant to develop mobility of the hands and feet and flexibility of the neck. But without a thought about speeding and the general erratic hazards I am subjecting us both to by making her talk, I have squeezed her dry of all her childhood memories of Brother Ossie. They will keep me company on the island. Tonight I shall sort them out and ponder over them.

We have to wait a few hours in a bar, the Chaperon Rouge, a delay due to our misinformed approach to the departure schedule of a ferry line which boasts of its unreliability. Over a long stretch of Tom Collinses, Silvana embarrasses me with her loud irrepressible laugh, but proves so entertaining that we barely make it to the boat in time, my beach bag and I. Silv waves good-by from her maroon convertible. I do not think that she can find her way back to the Bronx and I would be ready to bet that she will call Ossie and plead for directions. I hope, for her sake, that he can move his tongue today.

The ferry ride lasts twenty sunny water-splashing minutes. Kismet is only a weekend place in June, and except for the food-store and bar-restaurant attendants, I will be alone on this fine Friday. All mine is the white windy beach. I find the house easily. I open closets till I find what I am looking for: Cass's black sweater. I bury my face in it.

This four-beds room can sleep seven or eight people of the kind who can swing if they have to. The deckchairs can be brought in from the terrace, and the coffee table indulged on. A few curlers of Sheil's, pink plastic rollers, are scattered on the linen chest, close to Annette's green terry-cloth hairband. Mere things hold no grudges. I wonder at a remnant of tuna-fish casserole, in the refrigerator, and decide to attribute it to Dave Bernheim, genius of the leftovers. The two dozen cans of beer must have been stored by his roommate, Harry with the unquenchable thirst, who only swaggers when sober.

Dazed by a long afternoon of sunbathing with no visitors on the beach except sea gulls, ants, and a few passing sand-buggies, I go to bed early with my vibrator, an untouched egg sandwich, and the tales of six-year-old Ossie's escapes from a violent home. Their father used to beat them every other day. Silvana did not move under the blows, so the "old man" would tire soon. Her sister Millie would scream and fight back. She always got the worst treatment. As for Junior, he ran away at the slightest danger signal and lived off the streets. Silvana insists that her way of keeping still under the lickings made a loser out of her. Millie grew up into a tornado, and Junior later found real hiding places: the uptown cellars where he would "take off" and the cells his stealing would lead him into.

I think of my apartment where he seemed to feel so safe, so out of reach, so smothered, between rugs and drapes, rolled into nothingness. Did I give him shelter and release? Not of the kind that would stop his running. For I also showed him how empty was that vacant shop I call my heart, how unwilling I was to prepare it for any grand opening. So maybe he decided to treat it as one of his schticks. Just another safe to blow.

The gang joins me early Saturday morning. It is a fair weekend, without a cloud. Dispossessed of our limbs and bodies in behalf of the sun, we assume trustingly that he will appreciate our devotion. You can be lazy with passion if you go far enough, if you surrender every nerve, every hair and its root, every inch of your backbone to the inner caress of heat.

Dave and his girl Joyce are the kitchen-white type that turn pork-chop pink and feverish by two o'clock and retire with dark prophecies about our own broiled-to-be fate.

We faintly stir from our apathy. Harry brings cigarettes from the house and a pitcher of gin and tonic, steamy cold, marvelous. Sheil kicks sand around Cass. She was the last one to show up this morning, on the boardwalk, perched on high-heeled sandals, clad in pink slacks, peeking haughtily from under a huge green straw monstrosity, carrying her two Siamese cats, White House and Grant's Tomb—Whoose and Groomb, for short—and, in a zippered plaid bag, a dozen corn-on-the-cob.

Harry has stories to tell about Mexico, one of Daniel's inexhaustible subjects. I settle down keenly, chin in hand, to listen and learn. But it seems all he saw of Mexico was a hippy young thing who had a way with white mice. She could sit on her own hair when she untied her braids, before siesta, and what she had been taught in convent made up for her witchy cooking. A woman can poison or distort a whole new country for the male traveler who innocently thinks he is getting the best welcome-offering those foreign skies can burden him with. If I remember Daniel's stories, his load was limited to his tourist's equipment: no tempting target for the Gods is Daniel.

I give Sheil a censored version of my *souvenirs de prison*—Readers' Digest style. People make me talk too much. It is starting to sound (to my own ears) as if I made the whole thing up. Sheil is thrilled, sympathetic, and awed, all at the wrong moments. I catch the right glimpses in Cass's eyes, and we communicate beyond words. Annette is in Milwaukee, visiting her family. Sheil and I can unwind. We do not have to be on our best detached behavior around Cass. I still miss watching Sheil's game of ignoring Annette, with a warrior's knowledge of enemies that are best avoided. She would not strike unless she had a good chance of making a kill, but she can sting, and sting she does, in a way that, I suspect, forces Cass's admiration even though it also vastly aggravates him.

I huddle, once in a while, in Cass's arms. The sun gives his skin the color of fried fowl. He has a boil on the left corner of his mouth, covered with a small band-aid, and his dark furry hair sticks up appealingly. He slithers forward on his stomach, between Sheil and me, looking more and more like an overgrown eleven-year-old, gifted with the unfair advantage of the stealthy baby ocelot. I would like to be around when the hunter sheds his own guts for a change. It is strange that I should be so concerned because he commits not. I have found my alter ego, and who am I to dispute the immunity that I share with him?

At night, in the bar, Dave and Joyce counting points, Sheil vamps the bartender, a blond gay hunchback. I sit, drinking beer, between Harry and the Snake, intent on filling up with the anaesthetic power of my surroundings: the acrid moving curtain of pipe smoke, the tittering of glass on glass, wood, metal, and teeth, the juke box roars and whines putting to sleep Monday's threat to my un-involved mortality.

Harry is almost drunk and debates pop art. His voice fits well in the cataleptic background I am dissolving into, but he expects an answer once in a while, and Cass, nudging my right elbow, helps me not to miss the cue and laughs at seeing me play the sponge again: that change he can detect, in the middle of any conversation where I suspiciously become all nodding agreement and faraway acquiescent stares. Not only does what is going on around me not disturb my trip to nowhere, it gives it wings and keeps it afloat.

Harry criticizes my form of graphic inspiration, closed to the outside world, self-devouring and undented by a mighty influence such as pop art, the sweeping revolution that I cannot afford to ignore if I want to renew my visions of anti-reality. Cass states that bottle lids and automatic washers belong in the kitchen. Harry denies there is such a thing as a kitchen. Just then, a blaring hully gully deflates all my gathered defenses, and con-sciousness rushes back in.

Half an hour later, Sheil cleanses her face and baby-talks over Grant's Tomb's ticklish genitals. Joyce, very conventional in flannel gown and ponytail, joins Dave in bed. Cass begs Sheil not to tell him how much she paid for the few ounces of silk chiffon that eventually will cover parts of her. Sheil tells us. There is some hesitation about who will share my bed, and Cass does not know whether he should bow to Harry's seniority. Considering the favors I have granted to Harry earlier in the evening, right before dinner to be exact, and with not much reward, I have no trouble choosing Cass to let me hole in against his chest. He has not once mentioned Ossie, and I love him for it. Sheil is peeling and has a slight fever. She wants not a drop of company.

Sunday is very hot. A huge barbecued brunch has us working in shifts, then packed all together on the terrace. Cass goes on the warpath, under our cheers, to evaluate possibilities at a close-by house inhabited by three lonely females. Sheil, her nose-tip twitching with delight, is already putting herself into Annette's cheated shoes, but Cass comes back without bravado, not much aroused. One of the girls is close to forty and looks it. The nicest one, a little blonde, is cross-eyed. And the third one is of the bowlegged kind to whom you sell stock.

We take photographs on the beach. Sheil, flipped over Cass's arms, is a challenge to the dead. The gang tries to scare me into believing that Daniel's boat has been seen around, and I peek through my dark glasses with a distressed wail and crawling skin.

Back to New York, by way of one boat, two trains, and a cab, we part two by two and one by one, stifled by the oily, fuming air. I sleep on a couch in Dave's studio, pushing Harry away every fifteen minutes. Harry is also roofless for the moment. I call Ossie four times before going to bed. No answer.

13

June 8th

"One hundred Center Street." My cab-driver asks me if I work there. I say: "Yes, of course." He looks relieved. I will take to my grave that urge to please and gratify men, not necessarily in the erotic department.

I stand in front of the criminal court. It is too early. I walk across the street and around the block to a luncheonette where I order coffee, toast, and scrambled. I have some trouble keeping my bouncing wig out of the eggs.

It is raining lightly when I go out. I walk slowly. I do not want my stockings to get splashed. I will be immaculate up to my knees for the judge.

One flight up. The hall is full of plain-clothed jesters and shabby families with black umbrellas. Everybody is winding his watch. Part nine is at the end of the hall. Here is the court that caters to my kind.

Ossie is not here. I look at the fire-extinguisher, think of Oss, and whisper: "Up your throat." I wait for him a few minutes and watch cops go in and out of the men's room.

I enter, facing rows of benches, crowded with girls,

their friends, their superintendents, their bartenders, their men, and their men's brothers. Two sit alone. You can tell right away they are not going to make it. The court is hidden from sight by a half-wall. Stern, sarcastic, interrogative voices are heard. I take a few letters out of my handbag and start reading what my sister-in-law wrote, early this month, about her Bible classes, her maid's infractions, and what my brother thinks should be done about "le grand Charles." I have been carrying that letter around for a couple of months, lacking courage to finish it. But I do not have the heart to throw it away either. I am mildly curious about the way a French middle-class wife functions between Church and Family.

A cheerful usher walks to me, asks for my name as if it was a favor just to be allowed to pronounce it, also for my lawyer's name, and adds not to worry: my case will be called only when notice is given to the court that Mr. Crezzione has arrived.

Mr. Crezzione is arriving, face pathetically pleated and starched. I wonder what his wife feeds him. I already know about the bed-fasting. Is a sick-looking lawyer a good asset? He sits next to me and opens his briefcase after lifting his tortured eyebrows at Ossie's absence.

Our case is called right away. I walk with Enzo up to the half-wall and past it. Enzo mumbles to me to take my sunglasses off. I am going to be blind. We sit behind a desk facing the judge. All I can see is a blurred white spot: his face. Paul Flint, closer, is standing a few steps away from my cops, his head somewhat lowered.

I hear Saul, the arresting officer, state how, on May twenty-third at one o'clock in the afternoon, he saw a man whom he later identified as Paul Flint, ring my doorbell, go up to my apartment, then walk out of the house at 1:35 P.M. He and his colleague then had a conversation with Mr. Flint, following which they came up to my apartment and arrested me.

Enzo gets up and starts questioning Paul.

"How did you meet Aimée Kovacs, the defendant?"

"At a cocktail party, two months ago."

"Were there any other people present, Mr. Flint?"

"I said: a cocktail party. I did not count the guests."

"Now, Mr. Flint, did you call the defendant on the phone during the morning of May twenty-third?"

"Yes, I did."

"Can you repeat the conversation that took place between you and the defendant?"

"I told her I would like to drop in and see her. She said it would be fine with her. She was busy painting, but she thought she would be finished early in the afternoon."

"Did you go and see the defendant in the afternoon?"

"Yes, Sir, I did. At one o'clock."

"What was the defendant wearing when she opened the door to you?"

"Well . . . something dark, I think."

"What took place in the defendant's apartment?"

"We first had a drink and talked about people we know."

"Was any sum of money mentioned by the defendant then?"

"No."

"Did something happen between you and the defendant?"

"Yes, Sir, we had intercourse."

"Are you married, Mr. Flint?"

"Yes, Sir."

"Did the defendant ask you for money then?"

"No, she did not."

"Did you leave right away?"

"No, I did not. We had . . . a little talk. She told me she was planning to leave for a boating trip the next day. We talked about boats for a while. She noticed my tan. She said her skin had a tendency to burn, the first days of exposure to the sun. I asked her if she had a hat to protect her face. She said that she had bought bathing suits and caps and beach dresses and everything, but she forgot to purchase a hat. I decided then that I was going to leave some money as a gift for her to buy a sun hat."

"Did the defendant ask you for that gift, or was it your idea?"

"It was my idea."

"Did you put the money in the defendant's hand?"

"I don't think so. I must have put it down on the table."

"How much was it?"

"A twenty-dollar bill and a five."

"Did the defendant say she was going to buy a hat with it?"

"Yes, she did."

"Another question, Mr. Flint: Did you see any paintings in the defendant's apartment?"

"Yes . . . quite a number of pictures on the walls in both rooms."

"Do you know whether they have been painted by the defendant?"

"She told me she was a painter when I met her."

"Now I will ask you again, Mr. Flint. Was money mentioned by the defendant at any time that afternoon?"

"Definitely not, Sir."

It is now the judge's turn to pitch in. He leans down and asks Paul pleasantly:

"Do you wear a hat in the sun, Mr. Flint?" The judge's voice, deep, mellow-throated, full of courtesy and concern, is a vibrant contradiction to my lawyer's high-pitched querulous nasal tone. Sharpened by my inability to distinguish facial features without my glasses, my nerves react acutely to the change of mood and I perceive in Paul Flint's voice still another latitude in his response to the judge. Gone is the slight arrogance he had donned to deal with Enzo. Reverence and total lack of ease are now *de rigueur*.

"Yes, your Honor, I always wear a hat in the sun."

"What kind of hat, may I ask?"

"Well, your Honor, it depends . . . I guess I have worn all kinds, mostly straw hats. Right now, I wear an old canvas hat when I am fishing or sunbathing on the deck of my boat."

While mentioning that most prized of his possessions, Paul's voice takes on a little more assurance.

"Will you describe that particular hat, Mr. Flint?"

"Well, it is sort of . . . round . . . with a stuck-up brim, and a ribbon about it. Like a fancy army cap, in fact. . . ."

"How much did you pay for this hat?"

Paul is getting red in the cheeks. Even I can see that. His face is a glowing GO! traffic light.

"Well, your Honor, I did not buy that hat."

"Oh, you mean, it was *also* a gift?"

"It was given to me by the army, your Honor, as a token of gratitude for my services during the Second World War."

213

"I see. So you cannot name a price for it. It is indeed invaluable. Well, well, well, let's come back to peacetime and civilian life. I have to admit, Mr. Flint, that the price of twenty-five dollars strikes me as being a little high for a mere beach hat, but we all know that ladies' outfits are sometimes more expensive than they *ought* to be . . . Mr. . . . er . . . Crezzione, you may proceed."

Enzo leads me up one step, two steps, half a dozen of them, to a seat on the left side of the judge's high desk, then asks me:

"Mrs. Kovacs, are you married?"

"Yes, I am."

"Would you please speak a little louder? Is your husband living with you?"

"Not at the moment."

"Where is he?"

"In Europe. He left the States last year."

"What are your means of existence, Mrs. Kovacs?"

"My husband supports me. He sends me money."

"Do you sell your paintings?"

"Occasionally. I have sold four this year."

"For how much money?"

"A little under four hundred dollars."

"Is it your intention to stay in this country, Mrs. Kovacs?"

"No, Sir."

"When do you plan to leave the States?"

"Next month."

"Will you go back to live with your husband?"

"Yes, I will."

"I have no more questions, your Honor."

I am declared not guilty. Not one person in court

doubts that I am a prostitute and a soft-spoken liar, but the setup was well arranged and every falsehood properly backed. I am close enough to the judge now to feel his eyes all over me. Is he evaluating how much the deal cost me? Is he comparing me with the girls whom he did sentence this month? The ones who were guilty of the worst crime: empty pockets.

Outside in the hall, with Enzo, I take a deep breath and exclaim: "Wasn't that too much!" He shrugs: ". . . Had me worried for a while."

Ossie springs at us and hugs me; Saul, the cop, joins the gang, beaming, plainly expecting congratulations. I look at one of the City's finest with such eyes on the rocks that he protests: "Hey, what have I done now?" Paul Flint *himself* walks up to me, takes my hand—I am too stunned to move—and tells me, his voice unhappy: "Have a good trip, Lily, I wish you luck." He looks at his hat, puts it back on his head, and goes away, upset.

I remind Enzo that I will be taking care of his fee soon. He untactfully states that if I need somebody to sit for one of those paintings, he will be delighted to fill the part. I answer that I am a bit tired of portraits and contemplate specializing in still lifes. Enzo departs without a look for Ossie.

I trot down the stairs, Ossie at my heels. It is raining on my wig. I walk with my hands in my pockets, suppressing a desire to whistle. A mysterious enjoyable meanness is creeping over me. Ossie says: "It's Paul Flint's turn to have the cops on his back. They know he's worth a few bucks and the dumb son of a bitch don't realize what he's in for."

I see a phone booth and stop, fishing for dimes.

"I am all clean, Cass. Because of a beach hat. I'll see you at the island."

"Sheil, everything O.K. Thanks, crumb bum, I know you mean it. Jesus Christ, I'm dead."

"May I speak to Jim Brent? This is Lily Duke from New York. Well yes, it's important, it's about the most . . . Jim? It's all over, darling. I'm supposed to be a good little girl. You'd better remember it, too."

"Ben, what do you think? They gave New York males a break. Sure, O.K. for tomorrow. No, not tonight. To-night, I have to sentence somebody. Yes, Sir, it's catchy."

"Allo, Silvana? Blow that candle down, girl, I made the judge's day."

"Dave, flip the fishbowl for me. Freedom, they say. I'll be around this afternoon to mess around the bags. How is sunburn?"

"Mr. Nelsh, please. It is Lily Duke. Daniel? You are talking to an honest woman."

. . . Ten minutes after midnight.

"Listen, sweet . . ."

A couple of flies are buzzing around in the studio. It is late. We have seen a stupid movie. It is little to say that the West was never won that way. But the theater was cool and we were drinking iced coke. We stopped holding hands after a while, they just did not fit together.

Ossie puts the fan to work close to my couch. I turn around over a sheet wet with perspiration. The TV is on. My TV.

I do not try to entice that man by showing my legs, in the joking way I used to have. Those days are done and over with. He is allergic to naked flesh, he much favors the bulges of his own veins shot full of crap. All I let him see tonight is my need to be looked at, straight in the eye. I will play my part and let him believe that I ignore whatever it is I have to pretend I want to learn.

"Lissen, sweet. I got somethin' to tell you, and it's gonna be no piece of cake. Remember when I tried to make you talk about the whippin's? I knew all about it, but I wanted you to take it off your chest, in your own words." As I lift my eyebrows at him, he shrugs, half-laughing, half-sneering. "Sure I knew all about it, you have the damnedest way of showing your cards in advance. You hide them whips in your linen chest, then you send me to that chest for sheets, 'cause you forget you put the sheets in the bathroom closet, but I remember 'cause I always know what's inside any bathroom closet, and I saw you hide the whips where the sheets should been. It must been sure easy, for that professor you was married to, to catch you cheatin'! I bet you were practic'lly takin' wet rubbers out of your pockets under his nose. Well, never mind that, now it's my turn to spill. I came close to it a coupla times, but I couldn't quite make it."

Come on, Ossie, say it. He drops his cigarette. I pick it up and stick it back into his vapid mouth. He smiles weakly.

"You been watchin' me. I know you, you rat. You act different. And I guess I been sort of obvious lately. I want to tell you before you leave for France an' I want to tell you before you make me tell."

The dumb son of a grocer's wife. . . . What does he think I have been doing all night? I have tried hard to shame the truth out of him. I am down to my last right hook. He is so full of dope that he is getting dull. Licked. As long as I thought he had it licked, I was looking up

217

to him. It is hard not to hate him for the mistake I made. Now that he is all ready to talk, I wish I could silence him and I laugh aloud. He does not notice it.

"You know, when you say I shouldn't keep Beans's works in the studio, and I shouldn't see so much of him an' Becky, I have a good answer: those shots of Beans gettin' off. It's God's truth I have a plan for them shots. There's not a photographer in town that wouldn't give his right hand to grab 'em. There's not a photographer in town who could have shooted the real thing, like I did. But I got another reason to keep close to Beans. That's where the shit comes in. Fact is I'm back on the stuff. Period. I started again a while ago. But this time I keep it small. I'm in control, see. Please, sweet, don't cry. It's been awful to keep it from you: to see you gettin' wise an' nasty, and it make a dead man out of me too. I can't show you no more how I feel, an' you comin' back all nice and tanned from the Island."

That just about finishes me off. My tan has as much to do with it all as Paul's, in court, this morning. As for my tears, I have that habit of crying for no reason at all. My mother used to say "crocodile tears . . ."

Ossie puts his arms around me. He smells of sweat. I wish he would let me go, but I do not fight him off. I will never know where I stand with him, or is it mostly on my head? I hate to deal with him the way I deal with myself, but it is happening and I cannot stop it. I suddenly dislike his white hairy belly, his chapped cracked lips, with the very loathing I keep for definite portions of my body after they have been misused.

And at the same time I am all ready to forgive him for what he may, and what he may not, have done against

218

me in that sick need he is magisterially understating right
now:

"I don't shoot much now, sweet, it would kill me just
like that. I don't shoot half of what I used to."

I ask stonily: "How do you get it?"

He is hurt: "You jokin' or somethin'?" I am injuring his
pride. "With the contacts I got, I don't even have to pay
no money for it. Not yet."

"Yeah. . . ."

"But I gonna stop, sweet. I wouldn't talk it over with
you if I hadn't made up my mind, now would I?" He has
to convince me. He goes on, scratching his left leg, up
and down, lovingly: "I got too much goin' for me, now
. . . I have those plans I told you about: getting money
from my wife's cousin to buy equipment. Just a coupla
cameras, first. I'd leave Sims and Nat an' start on my own.
Keepin' my own clients. You know Sims owe me money
too. Maybe I could still use the darkroom in here, at night,
if they let me. I bet Nat wouldn't mind. I'd split with
them thirty per cent. It'd be worth it. I can do all that
only if I'm clean."

Mice are jumping above our heads in the fourth floor
warehouse. I am filing my nails. Ossie goes on, cracking
his knuckles:

"I also have to change my wife's mind. She don't see
enough of me to be sure I'm back on the stuff, but she
sure has her doubts, and she been listening to the sneaky
doctor that checks on me once in a while. And she make
it hard for the kids those days to be with me as much as
they want to."

I slap him across the knuckles with my emery board,
to stop him: "Cut out on the family crap and tell me when

you intend to stop with so many all-American reasons."

"I'm tellin' you. I need four days to clean up and a hole to crawl in. Like a full weekend with Monday and Tuesday, too. Right now I can't take even one day out, with Sims' work to finish for him. The swine promised Gregg a bunch of color prints. He hasn't touched them yet. I haven't seen the bastard do a solid hour's work for two weeks. I'll be breakin' my nuts over that job."

I reach for the hair brush and start fluffing the hair spray out of my hair. Ossie's nails start on his other leg. I offer my file. He discards it.

"You see, sweet, it's just a question of time. The will is there, it's the main thing. I know it'll be hell once more, but what else is new? I been there already."

"Will Beans give you a hand?"

I am being sarcastic, but that goes way over his head. "Well, Beans is in the can, I thought I tol' you. I'll manage by myself. Once I done it with Silv. It was messy. I'd hate to have her go through the bit again. She been drinkin' too much lately and she talktalktalks. I wouldn't want her to shoot her mouth off about it after it's done. Not that she'd mean to. But word would get to my wife, like one, two, three. You don't know my family! Pia, that's my wife, she take everything out on the kids, like my people used to do."

I breathe in and out a couple of times, hard and deep, and I tell him: "I will stay with you."

"You? You're nuts. You don't know what it's like."

"I will learn." I add, to make him mad: "I saw a movie about it."

That does it, but beautifully.

"Oh yeah? Lissen to her . . . I'm not a goddamn Frank

Sinatra. I'd curse you and kick you for real. I'd yell at you. I'd roll on the floor. You'd have to force me to drink and to go to the bathroom . . . take care of me like a baby."

Nothing will dampen my zeal: "I will manage. I got loads of free time, now: Sheil is taking care of my Johns. I'll tie your hands before you become dangerous. I will put you in rubber pants. I will gag you if you yell too much. Besides, I saw that movie twice."

He screams: "Forget that frigging movie, will you? I don't wanna you see me like that. I just don' wanna to."

I get up, feeling myself turning white: "Don't push me too far, Ossie. I will not have you alone in this. Not if I can help it. You don't want me to see you like this? It's just too bad, baby. How do you want me to see you? Falling down your chair? Sucking your own tongue? Dropping things? Sleeping on your feet? Burning your hand and not feeling it? Nodding, yawning, scratching, sniffing, twitching? I have news for you: I had a bellyfull of it. I'd rather see you roll on the floor and scream and suffer like hell. I may even enjoy it."

Ossie knows when to dissolve into thin air. He does not say: "You win, you rat." He turns the TV off and lies on his cot, fully dressed. His voice is soft: "Sleep well, sweet." I grunt at him: "You nightcrawler, you."

Sleep, Ossie, sleep. I will tend to you and rock your shifty head. For the last time. I will see you through the rituals of "withdrawal"—a good enough namesake for both our lives. You know, and I know, there is no cure for you. Whatever must be wasted shall be wasted. You will never wear the shining armor, you, my soiled knight in knave's clothing. The Round Table is not set for you, and as I crouch under its legs, dog fashion, looking for crumbs, I must face that my words, my thoughts, my feelings, all spell the name of an absent.

My plane ticket is in my purse. I will be leaving in ten days. I think of my Michel's grubby-strong growing boy's fingers. Ten fingers. Ten days.